MW00559707

PHYSC 167 (Solar System)
Course Book

Professor Laurel Robinson

PHYSC 167 (Solar System) by Laurel Robinson is licensed under a Creative Commons Attribution 4.0 International License.

Published by SUNY OER Service

SUNY Office of Library and Information Services
10 N Pearl St
Albany, NY 12207

Distributed by State University of New York Press

"Solar System Book Cover", Photos from Flickr — compiled by Elaine Farrally-Plourde, licensed under CC0
All images — CC0 Creative Commons Universal License

ISBN: 978-1-64176-069-0

A note to the reader:

This book is designed to provide an interactive learning experience. Just as you cannot learn to hit a baseball by simply reading about it or watching someone else do it, you cannot learn science by simply reading about it or watching someone else do it! Thus each chapter in this book is followed by an activity. The activity is integral to understanding the material; it is meant to enhance and test your understanding of what you read, correct any misconceptions you may have, and give you practice with answering questions on the material.

Additionally, at the end of each chapter there are three features you may find helpful:

The section called "Questions You Should Be Able To Answer" is a list of questions that you should be able to answer after reading the chapter. This is the basic information you should have gotten out of the chapter. I suggest that you read these questions *before* reading the chapter, so that you go into the reading knowing what information you need to look out for. Then write out the answers to these questions either during or immediately after reading.

The section called "Suggestions for Further Reading" provides links to internet resources where you can go to either obtain further information on a topic, read the same information on a topic but presented in a different way, or obtain further practice questions on a topic.

The section called "Comment Pitfalls" lists some of the common misunderstandings that students often have concerning the chapter material. You should read these common pitfalls and watch out for them in your own thinking!

Chapter 1: Classifying Solar System Objects

In this chapter, you will learn how scientists classify objects in the solar system. You will see how scientists define a planet, what the difference between a Terrestrial planet and a Jovian planet is, and how other objects, like dwarf planets, are defined.

As you read this, you are sitting somewhere on the planet Earth. Earth is one of the eight planets that orbit the Sun in our solar system. In order from closest to the Sun to furthest, those planets are Mercury, Venus, Earth, Mars, Jupiter, Saturn, Uranus, and Neptune. At one time Pluto, which orbits beyond Neptune, was also considered a planet; however it is no longer considered so. We will see why shortly. Our Sun is but one of hundreds of billions of stars which make up our galaxy, the Milky Way Galaxy. Finally, our galaxy is but one of hundreds of billions of galaxies in the universe!

Of course, ancient Greek and Roman astronomers did not know this. All these astronomers knew was that when they looked up at the sky, there were pinpricks of light. They noted that these pinpricks of light remained in the same patterns and did not move relative to one another (this is why we can define constellations – because the stars that make up the Big Dipper, for example, are always in the same place in reference to one another). However, they also noted that there were a few pinpricks of light that did not obey this rule; these pinpricks of light moved around against the background pattern of stars. Thus they called these pinpricks of light "planets" (meaning "wandering star" in Greek) and named them Mercury, Venus, Mars, Jupiter, and Saturn after their gods.

As science progressed, scientists realized that planets are actually balls of rock and/or gas that orbit the Sun. And as telescopes were invented and advanced, we discovered three more planets: Uranus in 1781, Neptune in 1846, and Pluto in 1930.

The problem (for Pluto!) arose around the turn of the millennium, when scientists suddenly began to find many more objects similar in size to Pluto (some even bigger) and in similar orbits as Pluto. Some of these objects are shown in Figure 1.1. Scientists were faced with a decision: either they needed to call all of these new objects planets as well, or they had to change the definition of a planet. They choose the later, and in 2006 the International Astronomical Union presented the new scientifically accepted definition of a planet.

Figure 1.1: Solar system objects with similar sizes and orbits as Pluto. (https://commons.wikimedia.org/wiki/File:TheTransneptunians_Size_Albed o_Color.svg)

According to this new definition, a planet is an object that (1) orbits the Sun, (2) is big enough to be round (> 1,000 km in diameter), and (3) has cleared its orbit of debris (think of a truck driving down the highway alone, versus a truck surrounded by other trucks and cars!). Pluto orbits the Sun and is big enough to be round, but because many other objects surround it, it has not cleared its orbit of debris. Thus Pluto is no longer considered a planet.

There are two types of planets: Terrestrial and Jovian. The differences can be seen on the plot in Figure 1.2 that shows the densities, sizes, and compositions of the planets. The Terrestrial planets are Mercury, Venus, Earth, and Mars. These are relatively small, rocky, high density planets with orbits that are closer to the Sun. The Jovian planets are Jupiter, Saturn, Uranus, and Neptune. These are relatively large, gaseous, low density planets with orbits that are further from the Sun. Unlike the Terrestrial planets, the Jovian planets have no solid surface, but they do have rings.

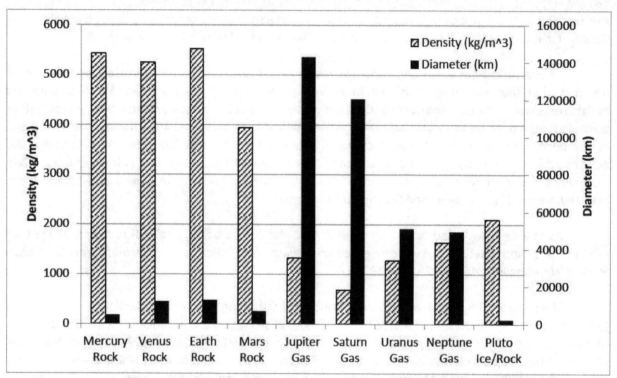

Figure 1.2: Densities, sizes, and compositions of the planets and Pluto.

What about Pluto? The International Astronomical Union (or IAU) defined a new category for Pluto: Pluto is a dwarf planet. A dwarf planet is an object that (1) orbits the Sun, (2) is big enough to be round (> 1,000 km in diameter), but (3) has NOT cleared its orbit of debris. Thus a dwarf planet satisfies the first two planet criteria but not the third.

What about objects that satisfy the first planet criteria but not the second or third? Such an object is called either an asteroid or a Kuiper Belt Object, depending upon where in the solar system it orbits. An asteroid is an object that (1) orbits the Sun between 2 and 5 AU (between Mars and Jupiter), (2) is NOT big enough to be round, and (3) is composed of rock. A Kuiper Belt Object (KBO) is an object that (1) orbits the Sun between 40 and 500 AU (beyond Neptune), (2) is NOT big enough to be round, and (3) is composed of rock and ice. Note that AU (Astronomical Unit) is a unit of distance: 1 AU = the distance between the Earth and the Sun = 93,000,000 miles. So a distance of 40 AU, for example, means 40 times further away from the Sun than the Earth is! Lastly, an object that orbits a planet or a dwarf planet is called a moon.

Figure 1.3 illustrates four expanding views of the solar system. Starting in the upper left, we have a view of the inner Solar System. Here we see the Sun and the orbits of the Terrestrial planets and Jupiter. Between the orbits of Mars and Jupiter lies the asteroid belt; asteroids are shown by dots in the image. Within the asteroid belt lies one dwarf planet (Ceres). Moving to the image in the upper right, the scale expands out to include Pluto. At this scale, the dots representing asteroids and the orbits of the inner planets are too small to pick out. However, we can see the orbits of the outer planets. Near Pluto and beyond lies the Kuiper Belt; Kuiper Belt Objects are shown by dots in the image. Additionally, there are about 50 different dwarf planets that lie within the Kuiper Belt. Some of these dwarf planets are much further away from the Sun than Pluto is. For example, the dwarf planet Sedna orbits the Sun in a very elliptical (oval) orbit that takes it as far away as about 937 AU from the Sun! The image in the lower right hand corner expands the view of the solar system to include Sedna's orbit. Lastly, surrounding the solar system there exists a spherical cloud of comets (which sometimes get bumped into the inner solar system where we can see them) called the Oort Cloud. The Oort Cloud marks the edge of the solar system and extends from about 50,000 to 200,000 AU. The image in the lower left hand corner expands the view of the solar system to include the inner edge of the Oort Cloud. Note that the Oort Cloud is so far away relative to everything else in the solar system that you can barely even see the orbit of Sedna in this image!

Figure 1.3: Four expanding views of the solar system, starting in the upper left and moving clockwise. (https://commons.wikimedia.org/wiki/File:Oort_cloud_Sedna_orbit.jpg)

Questions You Should Be Able to Answer

1. What is a planet (according to the IAU)?
2. Why is Pluto NOT a planet? How should Pluto be classified?
3. What is the difference between a Terrestrial planet and a Jovian planet? Name the Terrestrial and Jovian planets of our solar system.
4. What is a dwarf planet?
5. What is an asteroid?
6. What is a KBO?
7. What is a moon?

Common Pitfalls

-How do you know whether an object has cleared its orbit of debris? To answer this question, look at the object's orbital distance from the Sun. If the distance is 2-5 AU (between Mars and Jupiter), the object is surrounded by asteroids and hence has NOT cleared its orbit. If the distance is 40-500 AU (beyond Neptune), the object is surrounded by KBOs and hence has NOT cleared its orbit. Anywhere else, the object HAS cleared its orbit.

-Just because an object is located within the asteroid belt or Kuiper Belt, does not mean it is necessarily classified as an asteroid or a KBO. Remember that asteroids and KBOs are not big enough to be round. So if you have a round object that is within the asteroid belt, for example, it is not an asteroid. It is a dwarf planet surrounded by asteroids!

Chapter 1 Activity: Classifying Solar System Objects

Part 1: Comparing Pluto to Terrestrial and Jovian Planets

The chart below shows the diameter, density, and composition of objects in the solar system. The objects' orbital distances from the Sun in AU are also listed below the compositions.

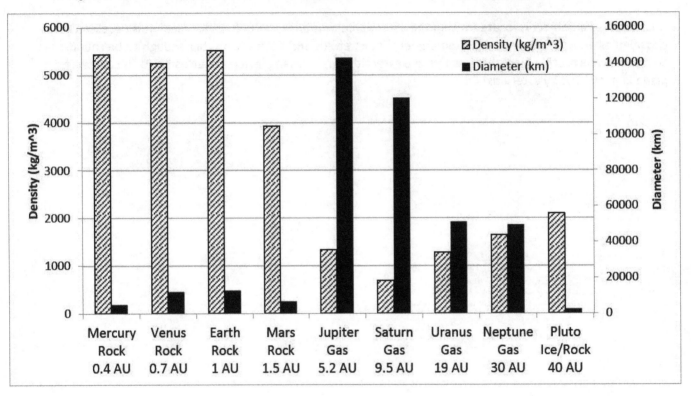

1. The Terrestrial planets are Mercury, Venus, Earth, and Mars. Using the chart above, circle the characteristics that the Terrestrial planets have in common.

high density	main composition is gas	large diameter	close to sun	rings
low density	main composition is rock	small diameter	far from sun	no rings

2. The Jovian planets are Jupiter, Saturn, Uranus, and Neptune. Using the chart above, circle the characteristics that the Jovian planets have in common.

high density	main composition is gas	large diameter	close to sun	rings
low density	main composition is rock	small diameter	far from sun	no rings

3. Pluto does not fit well into either group. It has characteristics similar to each group, and characteristics similar to neither group. List them below.

similar to Terrestrial planets:

similar to Jovian planets:

not similar to either Terrestrial or Jovian planets:

4. Given your answer to 3, does it make sense to you to call Pluto a planet (i.e. does it fit into one of the two groups)? Why or why not?

In 2006, the International Astronomical Union defined a planet as an object that:

1. orbits the Sun
2. is big enough to be round (small objects, less than ~1000 km, are lumpy/potato shape)
3. has cleared its orbit free of debris*

*Note that there are two belts of debris in the solar system: the asteroid belt (located between 2 to 5 AU, between Mars and Jupiter) and the Kuiper Belt (located further out, 40 to 500 AU). An object that is located within these regions is surrounded by debris, and hence has not satisfied the third criteria.

5. Given the above information, can we classify Pluto as a planet? Why or why not?

Part 2: Comparing Pluto to other Solar System Objects

A KBO is an object that:

1. orbits the Sun between 40 to 500 AU (beyond Neptune)
2. is not big enough to be round
3. is composed of rock and ice

6. Given this information, is Pluto a KBO? Why or why not?

A dwarf planet is an object that:

1. orbits the Sun
2. is big enough to be round
3. has not cleared its orbit free of debris

7. Given this information, is Pluto a dwarf planet? Why or why not?

8. Student A says, *"Pluto orbits the Sun at a distance of 40 AU, which is within the Kuiper Belt. This means that Pluto must be a Kuiper Belt Object."*

Student B says, *"But Kuiper Belt Objects are not big enough to be round and Pluto is 2,000 km in diameter, plenty big enough to be round. That means that Pluto must be a planet."*

Student C says, *"But remember that there is a third criteria that has to be met for an object to be considered a planet. A planet must orbit the Sun and be big enough to be round, but a planet must also have cleared its orbit of debris. Pluto is at 40 AU, which is within the Kuiper Belt. This means that Pluto is surrounded by Kuiper Belt Objects so it can't have cleared its orbit of debris. I think this means that Pluto is a dwarf planet that is within the Kuiper Belt.*

With which student(s) do you agree and why?

Part 3: Classifying Solar System Objects

Circle the correct statements to classify each object.

Description	Orbits the Sun?	Big Enough to be Round?	Cleared Orbit of Debris?	Classification
Ceres orbits the Sun at 2.8 AU. A picture of Ceres is shown below.	yes / no	yes / no	yes / no	planet / dwarf planet / asteroid / KBO / moon
Mathilde orbits the Sun between Mars and Jupiter and has a diameter of 50 km.	yes / no	yes / no	yes / no	planet / dwarf planet / asteroid / KBO / moon
Ida orbits the Sun at 2.9 AU. A picture of Ida is shown below.	yes / no	yes / no	yes / no	planet / dwarf planet / asteroid / KBO / moon
Eris orbits the Sun at 96 AU and has a diameter of 2,400 km.	yes / no	yes / no	yes / no	planet / dwarf planet

				asteroid KBO moon
Europa orbits Jupiter. A picture of Europa is shown below. 	yes no	yes no	yes no	planet dwarf planet asteroid KBO moon
Salacia orbits the Sun at 42 AU and has a diameter of 900 km.	yes no	yes no	yes no	planet dwarf planet asteroid KBO moon

Chapter 2: Solar System Sizes

In this chapter, you will gain a better understanding of the relative sizes of objects in the solar system and of their spacing.

Suppose I show you a picture of the Earth and Moon that looks like the image shown in Figure 2.1, and I ask you what is wrong with this picture?

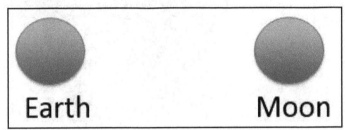

Figure 2.1: Earth-Moon System

You probably immediately thought something like "the Earth and the Moon are the same size" or "the Earth should be bigger than the moon." And you're right. If I want to make an accurate picture of the solar system, it should maintain correct relative sizes.

If you take the diameter of the Earth and divide it by the diameter of the Moon, you get about 4. This means that 4 Moons, lined up side by side, could fit across the diameter of the Earth. So if I want to draw a correct picture, I need to make my picture of the Earth 4 times bigger than my picture of the Moon, such as is done in Figure 2.2. As another example, if I were choosing objects to represent the Earth and the Moon in a 3-D model, I would need two objects that have a size difference of 4. So for instance a 12 inch basketball and a 3 inch baseball would work.

You might now think the picture in Figure 2.2 looks correct, but it's not. That's because although the relative sizes are correct, the relative distances are not. It turns out if you take the distance between the Earth and the Moon and divide by the Earth's diameter, you get 30. This means that you can fit 30 Earths between the Earth and the

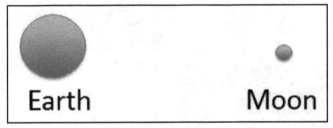

Figure 2.2: Earth-Moon System

Moon. Your picture should take this into account. However, in the figure in 2.2 we can only fit about 2 and a half Earths between the Earth and the Moon! In figure 2.3, we finally have an accurate picture of the Earth and the Moon. We would call this picture a "scale model" because it maintains relative sizes and distances. The Earth is 4 times bigger than the Moon AND you can fit 30 Earths between the Earth and the Moon. As another example, if we wanted to make a 3-d scale model of the Earth and the Moon we could take the basketball and the baseball from above and separate them by 30 feet.

Figure 2.3: Accurate Scale Model of the Earth-Moon System

Shown in Figure 2.4 are the relative sizes of the Terrestrial planets. Earth is the largest terrestrial planet, Venus is just slightly smaller, Mars is about half the Earth's size, and Mercury is about a third the Earth's size. To give you a sense of the Earth's size, the diameter of the Earth is about 8,000 miles. Its circumference is about 25,000 miles. If you drove nonstop at 60 mph, it would take you about 17 days to cover that distance!

Figure 2.4: Terrestrial Planets to Scale (https://commons.wikimedia.org/wiki/File:Star-sizes.jpg)

This may sound big, but the Jovian Planets are even bigger. Shown in Figure 2.5 are the relative sizes of all of the Jovian Planets compared to the Earth. Jupiter's diameter is about 11 times bigger than the Earth's; meaning that 11 Earths lined up side by side would fit across Jupiter. Saturn is slightly smaller than Jupiter. Lastly, Uranus and Neptune are both about 4 times larger in diameter than the Earth.

Figure 2.5: Earth and Jovian Planets to Scale (https://commons.wikimedia.org/wiki/File:Star-sizes.jpg)

However, none of the planets compare in size to the Sun (Figure 2.6). If we add the Sun to our picture, we see that it's about 110 times larger in diameter than the Earth; in fact, you can hardly see the Earth in this picture. Looking at this picture, it should be unsurprising that the Sun contains 99.86% of all of the mass in the solar system. In terms of volume, you could fit 1.3 million Earths inside the Sun!

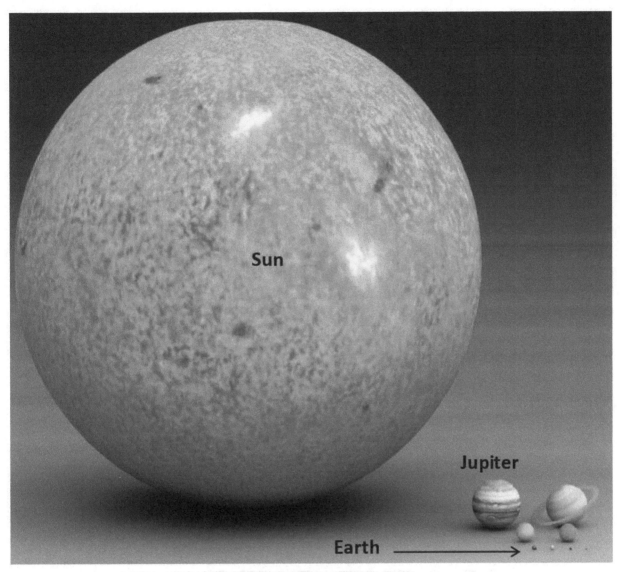

Figure 2.6: Planets and Sun to Scale
(https://commons.wikimedia.org/wiki/File:Planets_and_sun_size_comparison.jpg)

What about distances? We often think of the planets as being evenly spaced from the Sun, but that is not that case. In fact the spacing of the planets is such that it is difficult to see all of the planets' orbits in one diagram. Figure 2.7 shows the planets' orbits to scale. The left side of the figure shows the planets' orbits out to Mars. The right side of the figure shows the planets' orbits from Mars to Pluto. All of the terrestrial planet's orbits would fit within the circle representing Mars' orbit.

Enlargement of inner solar system

View looking down from above the Sun

Figure 2.7: Planet Orbits to Scale (http://www.nasa.gov)

Table 2.1 shows the actual distances of the planets from the Sun and their diameters. The distances are given in AU. An AU is an astronomical unit. 1 AU is equal to the distance between the Earth and the Sun, which is 93 million miles (if you could drive between the Earth and Sun, even driving nonstop at 60 mph would take you 177 years). So since Uranus has a distance of 19 AU, this means that it is 19 times further from the Sun than the Earth is.

Planet Name	Distance (AU)	Diameter (km)
Mercury	0.387	4,879
Venus	0.723	12,104
Earth	1.000	12,742
Mars	1.524	6,779
Jupiter	5.203	139,822
Saturn	9.537	116,464
Uranus	19.191	50,724
Neptune	30.069	49,244

Table 1.1: Distances and Diameters of the Planets

For comparison, the closest star (Alpha Centauri) to the Sun is about 276,000 AU away. The closest large galaxy (Andromeda Galaxy) to our galaxy is about 158,000,000,000 AU away. Imagine for a moment that our Sun were a basketball. Then the Earth would be a bb-bun ball 110 feet away, Pluto would be a speck of dust 0.8 miles away, Alpha Centauri would be a basketball in London (assuming you are currently in NYC), and the nearest galaxy would be out in the asteroid belt.

14

Questions You Should Be Able to Answer
8. What is a scale model?
9. You should have a general idea of the sizes and distances in the solar system.

Suggestions for Further Reading
1. http://www.scalesolarsystem.66ghz.com/#saturn (scale model example)
2. http://thinkzone.wlonk.com/SS/SolarSystemModel.php (scale model calculator and map)

Chapter 2 Activity: Size and Scale of the Solar System

The table below lists the distances (from the Sun) and the diameters of each of the planets in our solar system. Use this table for reference throughout this activity.

Planet Name	Distance (AU)	Diameter (km)
Mercury	0.387	4,879
Venus	0.723	12,104
Earth	1.000	12,742
Mars	1.524	6,779
Jupiter	5.203	139,822
Saturn	9.537	116,464
Uranus	19.191	50,724
Neptune	30.069	49,244

Part 1: A Scale Model of the Earth and the Sun

1. The Sun has a diameter of about 1,400,000 km. How many Earth's, lined up side-by-side, would fit across the diameter of the Sun?

2. The distance between the Earth and the Sun is 1 AU. This is equal to 150,000,000 km. How many Suns, lined up side-by-side, would fit in the distance between the Earth and Sun?

3. Suppose that you create a scale model of the solar system using a 1-ft diameter basketball to represent the Sun. How far away from the basketball should you place the object representing the Earth?

4. Suppose that you use a 1-ft diameter basketball to represent the Sun and a 4-inch diameter ping-pong ball to represent the Earth, and you place these objects 110 ft apart. Is this an accurate scale model of the Earth-Sun system?

5. Two students are discussing their answers to the previous question:

Student A says, "*I think it is an accurate scale model. You can fit 110 Suns between the Earth and the Sun. In this model, each Sun is 1 ft. Thus 110 Suns is 110 ft, so the scaled distance is correct – you could fit 110 basketballs (Suns) between the basketball and the ping-pong ball (the Earth and the Sun).*"

Student B says, "*But what about the relative sizes? I thought that an accurate scale model needs to have correct relative distances AND sizes. You can fit 110 earths across the Sun, but you can't fit 110 ping-pong balls across a basketball! I think the object representing the Earth needs to be smaller.*"

With which student(s) do you agree, and why?

6. Suppose that you create a scale model of the solar system using a 1-ft diameter (12-inch) basketball to represent the Sun. About how big in inches should the object representing the Earth be?

Part 2: Creating a Scale Model of the Solar System

6. Imagine that we are creating a scale model of the solar system using a 1-ft diameter basketball to represent the Sun. Fill in the table below giving the scaled distance and scaled size in the model. Then choose a appropriate representative object for each planet. You can choose from the objects listed below. The Earth has been done for you as an example.

-basketball: 12 inches
-baseball: 3 inches
-ping pong ball: 1.5 inches
-marble: 0.5 inches
-bb gun ball: 0.1 inches
-sand grain: 0.01 inches

Planet Name	Distance (AU)	Diameter (km)	*Scaled Distance*	*Scaled Size*	*Representative Object*
Mercury	0.387	4,879			
Venus	0.723	12,104			
Earth	1.000	12,742	*110 ft*	*0.11 in*	*bb gun ball*
Mars	1.524	6,779			
Jupiter	5.203	139,822			
Saturn	9.537	116,464			
Uranus	19.191	50,724			
Neptune	30.069	49,244			

7. At then end of this activity, there is a map of campus. A dashed line has been drawn on this map; the line starts at Hartford Hall, proceeds down the hill to the Library, passes between the TECH building and the Student Center, and ends at the Physical Education building. Suppose that you place the basketball representing the Sun in Hartford Hall. Using the scale bar on the map, mark where on the line you would place each of the objects representing the planets. If any of the planets do not fit on the map, indicate which ones here!

8. Pluto is about 40 AU from the Sun. Calculate Pluto's scaled distance from the Sun in this model. Will Pluto fit on the campus map? If so, mark it.

9. The nearest star to our Sun is Alpha Centauri. Alpha Centauri is 4.37 light years from the Sun. A light year is a unit of distance equal to 63,241 AU. How many AU is Alpha Centauri from the Sun?

10. Calculate Alpha Centauri's scaled distance from the Sun in this model. Will Alpha Centauri fit on the campus map? If so, mark it. If not, where would it be (give a location)? Note that there are 5,280 feet in a mile.

Chapter 3: Studying the Planets

In this chapter, you will learn how scientists study objects in the solar system. You will learn how science is defined, how the scientific method works, and the difference between a hypothesis and a theory. Then you will learn how scientists apply the scientific method to learn about the planets, and the different types of robotic space missions they use.

Science is hard to define because it is both knowledge and a process. By knowledge, I mean that science is what we know about the world; in other words, all of the things you read about in your science textbooks: the general principles that operate in the world, as we have discovered through observation and experimentation. Things like Newton's Laws and the Theory of Evolution. By process, I mean that science is the process we use to obtain this knowledge; in other words, the scientific method.

An alternative way to attempt to define science is to look at its characteristics (see Figure 3.1). The first characteristic is that science focuses on the natural world (things like atoms, plants, galaxies, and the force of gravity). Unobservable supernatural phenomenon (things like ghosts, souls, and God) are not allowed because they don't operate according to the known rules that govern the natural world and therefore can't be studied. Not only does science focus on the natural world, but it aims to explain that world. For instance, science tries to answer questions like why we have earthquakes and why the planets all look different from one another. The third characteristic is that science uses testable ideas. For an idea to be testable, it must generate specific predictions that would be born out if the idea were true (we will discuss this more later). Next, science relies on evidence. This means that ideas in science have data to back them up. Fifth, science involves a community of scientists working together to come to a consensus – it is not just one person working alone. A lot of science is done in collaborations, with groups of scientists working together. Furthermore, a scientific idea is not considered useful until it has been presented to, validated by, and used by other scientists. Next, science leads to ongoing research. This means it will never be finished – there will always be more ideas to explore and to test. And lastly, science benefits from scientific behavior. This means that science works best when scientists behave in an ethical manner; they should be open about exposing their ideas to testing, should be sure to give appropriate credit to other scientists' work, should not suppress data that does not fit their ideas, and so forth.

Science...

- focuses on the natural world
- aims to explain the natural world
- uses testable ideas
- relies on evidence
- involves a community
- Leads to ongoing research
- benefits from ethical behavior

Figure 3.1: Science Characteristics

So what can science do? Well, science seeks to explain and make predictions about the natural world. However, it is important to understand that science will never uncover a 100% correct and finished model of the world. This is not possible because all science is tentative. There is always another test that you can do, and there is always a chance that that test will change your ideas. In short, we can say that science gives us a model of nature that is accurate (meaning it fits our observations) and is useful (meaning we can use the model to make reliable predictions). For example, Newton's Laws are accurate in that they fit all of our observations about the motions of objects, and they are useful in that we can use them to make reliable predictions, like how much fuel you need to send a rocket to the moon!

You have probably seen the scientific method represented as a linear series of steps in the past (such as in Figure 3.2). However, this isn't really an accurate illustration of how science works. All of these steps, like constructing a hypothesis and doing experiments, are important parts of science, but in reality science is not done in any particular order and there are lots of dead ends.

It is better instead to represent the scientific method in a diagram as shown in Figure 3.3, which shows all of the parts involved, but in no specific order. At the heart of science is testing ideas. This is what science is all about: gathering and interpreting data to test the validity of an idea (note that in science, ideas are known as hypotheses). At the periphery of the diagram, we have several other important parts of science. At the top is exploration and discovery – this is where scientists observe, read, ask questions, and in general search for inspiration. In the bottom right is community analysis and feedback. This is the community endeavor part of science, where a scientist gets feedback from her peers through conferences, publications, and discussions. Lastly in the bottom left is benefits and outcomes. This is why we do science in the first place. To develop new technology, solve problems, address, societal issues, inform policy, and build a new knowledge.

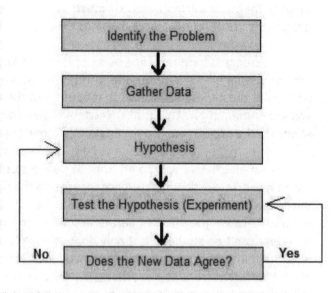

Figure 3.2: Too Simple A View of the Scientific Method (https://commons.wikimedia.org/wiki/File:The_Scientific_Method.jpg)

Figure 3.3: Scientific Method

Focusing on hypotheses, a hypothesis is an explanation of a phenomenon. A good hypothesis should be both testable and evidence-based. Testable means that a hypothesis should make a prediction that can be tested through experiments or gathering new data. For example, one could make a hypothesis that plants need water to grow. You could test this via an experiment – try to grow plants without water and see what happens. Of course, you'll find the plants will not grow, and your hypothesis will be supported. An example of a hypothesis that would not be testable is that ghosts help plants to grow. This is not testable because (despite what you may see on TV) there is no way to test for the presence of ghosts! Evidence-based means that it is supported by the majority of the current data we've collected. Note that a hypothesis could be evidence-based at one point in time, but could be rejected later if new data is collected that conflicts with the hypothesis' predictions.

Many people confuse hypotheses and theories. But these concepts have very specific and different meanings in science. In science, a hypothesis is just an idea. You can call something a hypothesis whether or not it has been tested yet. A theory, on the other hand, is a model of some piece of nature that has been tested many many times and has passed all of the tests so far. Theories therefore have tons of evidence to support them. When scientists say that evolution is a theory, what we mean is that there is a lot of evidence and experiments in support of that idea. Additionally, theories tend to be broader in nature than hypotheses; they explain a wide range of phenomena.

Going back to the scientific method, let's focus on gathering and interpreting data to test a hypothesis. How do we do this when the objects we are studying are millions of miles away, like the planets?

Figure 3.4: Ancient Chinese Star Map
ps://commons.wikimedia.org/wiki/File:Su_Song_Star_Map_1.JPG)

The simplest way to go about this is naked eye observation. Go out at night, look at the sky, and track the motions of objects over the course of the night, the week, the month, the year, and so forth. Astronomers have been doing this for centuries. For example, the Mayans built their temples around celestial events. They would design their temples so that the stars and the Sun would appear in certain places around the temple at special times of the year. Additionally, the Chinese developed very detailed star maps (Figure 3.4), and the Greeks developed sophisticated models of the solar system.

To learn more, one needs telescopes to see objects that are too dim to be visible to the naked eye. The first telescopes were developed in the early 1600s and were little more than giant spyglasses. Today's telescopes are highly advanced and allow us to see even to distant galaxies.

Scientists also study the solar system using experiments. For example, Figure 3.5 shows a picture of a lab that was built at the NASA Johnson Space Center in Houston, Texas to study the rocks from the moon that were brought back by the Apollo astronauts. The lab is a "clean lab" to prevent contamination of the rocks with Earth materials: workers and visitor must be decontaminated and wear special clothing to enter the room, and the rocks are kept in special containers and only touched through gloves. Sometimes problems are so broad in scale that scientists need to do experiments on the computer; Figure 3.6 shows an example of a simulation to study what happened during the asteroid impact that led to the extinction of the dinosaurs.

Figure 3.5: Moon Rock Lab at Johnson Space Center (sciencemag.org)

Figure 3.6: Computer Simulation of a Collision Between Two Asteroids (Laurel Senft and Sarah Stewart-Mukhopadyay)

24

An additional way that scientists can study the solar system is using meteorites. Meteorites are rocks that fall to Earth from space. Most meteorites come from the asteroid belt. However, some asteroids actually come from other places, like Mars or the Earth's Moon!

While naked eye observations, telescopes, experiments, and meteorites give us some information about the solar system, MOST of our information about the solar system comes from space exploration: both manned space missions and robotic space missions. To date, three countries have sent humans into space: The Soviet Union, The United States, and China.

The US manned space program can be broken down into 6 main programs. The Mercury program, from 1959-1963, put humans into space and into orbit around the Earth. The Gemini program, from 1963-1966, practiced skills (like spacewalks) that would be needed to send astronauts to the moon. The Apollo program, from 1961-1972, put humans on the moon. Skylab, from 1973-1974, was the first American space station. The Space Shuttle was a reusable space vehicle which we used from 1981-2011. Lastly, the International Space Station is a large research space station currently in use. Astronauts used to be shuttled back and forth to the International Space Station via the Space Shuttles, but now a Russian vehicle, called Soyuz, is used instead.

The pinnacle of the manned American space program was Apollo. Since then, manned space program has dropped off in favor of robotic space missions. The simple reason for this is funding: NASA's budget dropped sharply following Apollo (NASA now receives less than 0.5% of the federal budget), and robotic space missions are much cheaper (and safer) than manned space missions.

There are six kinds of robotic space missions that we've used to explore the solar system: they are flybys, orbiters, landers, rovers, sample returns, and impactors. We will go through each type in turn.

Figure 3.7: The Voyager Spacecraft
(https://commons.wikimedia.org/wiki/File:Voyager)

Before we do so, however, let's look at the kinds of instruments spacecraft can carry. They can carry cameras of various resolutions to take pictures. They can also carry spectrometers, which are instruments that measure the kinds and amounts of light coming off of a surface. This allows us to determine compositions (like the minerals and rocks that make up a surface, or the gases in an atmosphere) because different substances have different spectroscopic signatures, analogous to the way different people have different fingerprints. Altimeters measure topography, magnetometers measure the size and direction of the magnetic field, seismometers measure motions of the ground (due to earthquakes), thermometers measure temperature, anemometers measure wind speed, and barometers measure atmospheric pressures. Lastly, all spacecraft will have radio transmitters and antennas to communicate with the Earth.

A flyby mission flies by an object (or several objects) and collects data along the way. Because the amount of data collected is limited, this kind of mission is good for reconnaissance. For example, suppose you want to explore an area of the solar system that has never been explored before and to take a little bit of data on a lot of objects to determine what is out there and what might be interesting for more detailed future study....a flyby would be ideal for this. Examples of flyby missions are the Voyager I and II missions (Figure 3.7), which were launched in 1977. These missions were the first to travel to the outer solar system and performed flybys of the Jovian planets and their satellites. A fun bit of trivia is that when scientists launched the Voyager missions, they recognized that the spacecraft would eventually drift away from our solar system and one day, tens of thousands of years from now, perhaps enter a different solar system and just maybe be found by intelligent alien life! Just in case this ever did happen, scientists included on each spacecraft a gold-plated phonograph record containing sounds and images selected to represent the diversity of life on Earth. The cover of the record contains images to help potential alien life decipher where the spaceship is from and to play the record. A sample of the statement left on the record by then-President Jimmy Carter reads: "This is a present from a small distant world, a token of our sounds, our science, our images, our music, our thoughts, and our feelings. We are attempting to survive our time so we may live into yours. We hope someday, having solved the problems we face, to join a community of galactic civilizations."

Now suppose you want more comprehensive data. Not just a few pictures of a planet, but maps of the entire surface. Then you would use an orbiter. Orbiters are put into orbit around a planet to collects lots of data over a long period of time. Not only does this give you a view of the entire planet, but it allows you to see any changes that may occur over time. An example of an orbiter mission is the Mars Global Surveyor, which was launch in 1996 and gave us a detailed view of Martian climate and geology.

For some measurements, you need to be actually on the surface. For example, you cannot measure wind speed or analyze a planet's soil unless you are sitting on the surface. Thus the next type of robotic space mission is a lander. Landers land on a planet but stay put once they land. This allows us to get an up-close detailed view of the surface. An example of a lander is Viking 1, which was the first lander on Mars (Figure 3.9).

Figure 3.8: Mars Global Surveyor (http://www.nasa.gov)

Figure 3.9: First Image Ever Taken from the Surface of Mars, taken by Viking 1 on July 20, 1976
(http://www.nasa.gov/)

Sometimes you not only want to land, but you want to move around as well. For this you would use a rover. Not only does this give you an up-close detailed view of the surface, but you can move to interesting things! Rovers cam typically move about 10 miles in a period of few years. An example is the Mars Exploration Rovers, Spirit and Opportunity (Figure 3.10), which were launched in 2003.

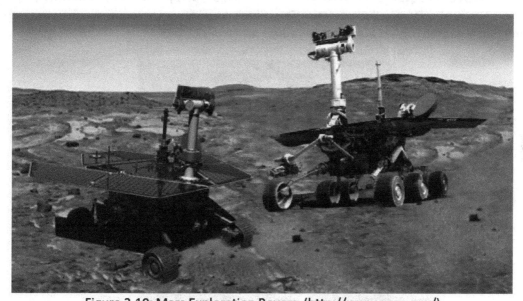

Figure 3.10: Mars Exploration Rovers (http://www.nasa.gov/)

The goal of a sample return mission is to bring stuff (like rocks or dust) back so that scientists can study it in labs here on Earth. So far, there have not been any sample return missions to other planets (due to cost and difficulty - you have to carry enough fuel to not only launch off of the Earth, but the destination planet as well); however, Stardust (Figure 3.11), which was launched in 1999, brought back comet dust.

Figure 3.11: Stardust (http://www.nasa.gov/)

Last, but not least is an impactor mission. In this type of mission, you have an object hit a surface and create an explosion. This allows you to see what lies underneath the surface. An example of this type of mission is the Deep Impact mission to comet Tempel 1 (Figure 3.12). This mission launched an impactor into the comet whilst a flyby collected data. This allowed scientists to determine the structure of the comet and figure out the comets are essentially dirty snowballs!

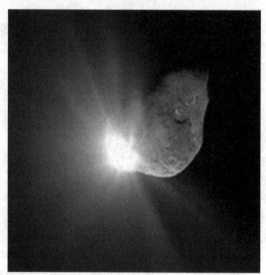

Figure 3.12: Impact Created by Deep Impact (http://www.nasa.gov/)

Questions You Should Be Able to Answer
1. How do we define science?
2. What are some of the important characteristics of science?
3. What can science do?
4. What can science <u>not</u> do?
5. Describe the scientific method. What is at the heart of the scientific method?
6. What is a hypothesis?

7. What makes a good hypothesis?
8. What is the difference between a hypothesis and a theory?
9. What are some ways to gather data bout the solar system?
10. Describe a flyby, orbiter, lander, rover, sample return, and impactor mission. What is each type of mission best suited for?

Suggestions for Further Reading
1. http://undsci.berkeley.edu/article/intro_01 (the scientific method)
2. http://www.nationalgeographic.com/125/timelines/space-exploration/ (space exploration timeline)

Chapter 3 Activity: Hypotheses

Part 1: Criteria for a Good Hypothesis

A good hypothesis should be _testable_. This means that you can think of experiments that could be conducted to collect data that would either support or refute the hypothesis. A good hypothesis should also be _evidence-based_. In other words, most of the data that has been collected concerning the problem should be consistent with your hypothesis.

Suppose that an alien on Earth is wondering why a rubber ball falls back down to the ground after it is thrown into the air. It comes up with several ideas about the ball.

    Hypothesis a - Gravity is pulling the ball downward.

    Hypothesis b - A mystical force that cannot be measured is pushing the ball down.

    Hypothesis c - Earth's magnetic field is pulling on the rubber ball.

Circle the correct answers below.

1) Which statement is NOT a good hypothesis because it is not testable?   a   b   c

2) Which statement is NOT a good hypothesis because, although testable, it is not supported by the majority of current data?   a   b   c

3) Which statement IS a good hypothesis?   a   b   c

Part 2: Analyzing Hypotheses

Analyze the hypotheses below. First indicate whether or not each is testable. Then indicate whether or not each is evidence-based (hint: if you can't test it, it can't be evidence-based!). Then indicate whether or not it's a good hypothesis (hint: it's only a good hypothesis if your previous answers were yes!).

Hypothesis	Testable? (write yes or no)	Evidence-Based? (write yes or no)	Good Hypothesis? (write yes or no)
1. David Beckham is the best soccer player of his generation.			
2. Several kilometers below its surface, Jupiter's moon Europa has an ocean of liquid water.			
3. Bacteria on Earth can survive at temperatures below freezing.			
4. Children born on Mondays score higher on the SATs than children born on other days of the week.			
5. Aliens can manipulate time so that they can abduct people and experiment on them without the people ever knowing.			

Provide your reasoning for 1 here:

Provide your reasoning for 2 here:

Provide your reasoning for 3 here:

Provide your reasoning for 4 here:

Provide your reasoning for 5 here:

Chapter 3 Activity: Missions

Part 1: Types of Missions

1. Match the type of mission with the correct description below. Your choices are: flyby, orbiter, lander, rover, sample return, and impactor.

Creates an explosion to observe the underlying surface.   _____

Lands on a surface but remains stationary.   _____

Brings material back to the Earth for study.   _____

Lands on a surface and can move around for short (~10 mile) distances.   _____

Collects small amounts of data as it goes by one or more objects.   _____

Goes in to orbit around an object to collect comprehensive data.   _____

2. Different missions are ideal for different purposes. Suppose that you wanted to send a mission to map the composition (rocks and minerals) of the surface of an entire planet. Which type of mission would you choose and why?

3. Student A says, *"I chose a rover mission because then you could get as close to the rocks as possible to figure out their compositions."*

Student B says, *"But rovers can't survey an entire planet; they can only go about 10 miles. So if you want to look at the entire planet, you need an orbiter mission."*

With which student(s) do you agree and why?

4. Which type of mission do you think would be best if you want to look at a large number of objects in an area you've never explored before (e.g. a reconnaissance mission)? Why?

5. Which type of mission do you think would be best if you wanted to place a weather station on a planet to track the weather over the course of a year?

6. Student A says, *"I chose an orbiter mission because then I could see as much of the planet as possible."*

Student B says, *"I think that to measure some aspects of the weather, like wind speed and temperature, you need to actually be in the atmosphere. So I chose a rover."*

Student C says, *"I agree that you need to be in the atmosphere, but I think being able to move around isn't necessary. The weather will be pretty much the same 10 miles away. So I chose a lander over a rover because it would be cheaper."*

With which student(s) do you agree and why?

Part 2: Choosing Between Missions
Pretend that you are on a budget committee and are choosing missions to fund. For each mission below, state whether you would fund it and why. Consider your knowledge of the planets as well as your knowledge of the types of missions.

7. An orbiter to Mercury to map the topography and learn more about the geology of the planet.

8. A rover to Titan to photograph the whole surface and understand the atmosphere and global environment.

9. A flyby to Jupiter to learn more about Jovian storms and study how they change over time.

10. A lander to Venus to study its volcanoes.

11. A lander to Europa to place a seismic station (like radar) to learn more about the thickness of the ice.

Chapter 4: The Copernican Revolution

In this chapter, you will learn how scientists developed an accurate model of the solar system. You will see the assumptions that were made by ancient astronomers and how a phenomena called retrograde motion challenged these assumptions. You will then see how Ptolemy and Copernicus explained retrograde motion using different models of the solar system.

You are probably aware that every day the Sun rises in the east, moves across the sky, and sets in the west. Figure 4.1 shows the path of the Sun over the course of a day; note that in this diagram you are looking south, so east is to the left of the page and west is to the right. At the beginning of the day, the Sun will rise in the east. It will move higher in the sky until it reaches its highest point in the southern sky at noon. Then it will descend and finally set in the west. Note that this is what they sun *appears* to do, but in *reality* the sun is not actually moving. The reason for the apparent motion is that the Earth rotates. The Sun itself doesn't move, but as the Earth rotates, the Sun will appear to move across the sky.

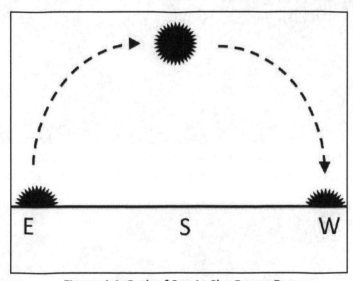

Figure 4.1: Path of Sun in Sky Over a Day

By the same logic, any other object in the sky that doesn't move over the course of a day will exhibit the same apparent motion. So not only does the Sun appear to rise in the east and set in the west, but every other object in the sky – like stars and planets – do so as well.

Of course ancient astronomers did not know this. Because we see things appear to move around the Earth, ancient astronomers believed that the Earth is the center of the solar system and that the Earth doesn't move.

However, this assumption leads to problem when trying to explain the way in which planets appear to move in the sky. Over the course of a single night, a planet will move with the stars, rising in the east and setting in west. However, over the course of weeks or months, the planet will move *relative* to the background stars. So though the planet will always move with the stars on any given day, it will be next to different stars as the weeks progress. Another way to think about this is if you take a picture of the sky at midnight one day, and then take a picture of the sky at midnight one week later, the stars will all be in roughly the same position and in the same patterns, but the planet will have moved.

Figure 4.2 shows the motion of Mars relative to the background stars during the summer of 2018. The image is looking south, so east is the left and west is to the right. Note that in general planets appear to drift west to east relative to the background stars. This is known as prograde motion. However, sometimes a planet will temporarily reverse direction and move from east to west. This is known as retrograde motion. Figure 4.3 shows the same picture as Figure 4.2, but the prograde motion is highlighted in light gray and the retrograde motion is highlighted in dark gray.

Figure 4.2: Motion of Mars Relative to Background Stars
(https://commons.wikimedia.org/wiki/File:Mars_motion_2018.png)

Figure 4.3: Motion of Mars Relative to Background Stars. Prograde motion is highlighted in light gray, and retrograde motion is highlighted in dark gray.

Retrograde motion cannot be explained by a model of the solar system where the planets orbit directly around the Earth. So in AD 140, the Greek astronomer Ptolemy developed a model of the solar system to explain this motion (Figure 4.4). This was the first mathematical model of the solar system. In this model, the Earth is at the center, and the sun and planets orbit around the Earth. However, the planets do not orbit *directly* around the Earth. Instead, they orbit around small circles (called epicycles) and the epicycles orbit the Earth. Because of this simultaneous rotation, the planet will sometimes move backwards in the sky (hence, retrograde motion). It should also be noted that Ptolemy's model didn't technically have the Earth directly at the center of the planets' orbits; he had a point slightly offset from the Earth that he called the "Center of the Deferent" at the center.

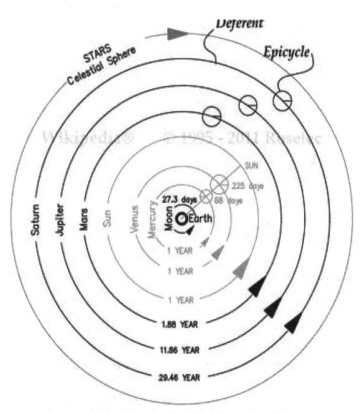

Figure 4.4: Ptolemy's Model of the Solar System
(https://upload.wikimedia.org/wikipedia/commons/8/82/De_revolutionibus-
Copernicus_Illustrates_Heliocentric_Order_of_Planets_not_Orbits.jpg)

While Ptolemy's model explained retrograde motion (Figure 4.5), it was a complicated model and became even more complicated. As data on the solar system improved, Ptolemy (and others) found that they had to add more and more epicycles to explain the data. For instance, instead of a planet orbiting on an epicycle, you have a planet orbiting an epicycle, which orbits on another epicycle, which orbits around the Earth. Late versions of Ptolemy's model had nearly 100 layered epicycles to explain the observations!

Figure 4.5: Ptolemy's Model Explains Retrograde Motion (apparent path of planet is dashed line)
(https://commons.wikimedia.org/wiki/File:Ptolemy_Epicycles.svg)

In the early 1500s, Copernicus realized that things would be a lot simpler if the Sun were at the center of the solar system. If you let the Sun be at the center, and let the planets that are closer orbit faster than the planets that are further, then retrograde motion results as a natural consequence.

This is illustrated in Figure 4.7. We have the Sun at the center (labeled S), and the orbits of Earth (inner circle) and Mars (outer circle) are shown. The position of the Earth (the numbered Ts) is shown at seven different times, as well as the corresponding positions of Mars (the numbered Ms), and the corresponding position of Mars relative to the background stars as seen from Earth (the numbers). Notice that Mars in general drifts towards the east relative to the background stars (prograde motion). However, because the Earth is moving faster, it eventually overtakes Mars in its orbit. When this happens Mars will appear as if it is moving backwards (retrograde motion). Note that it is not actually moving backwards; it just looks that way. This is just like when you are in a car and you approach and overtake a slower car on your right. If you look over at the slower car at the moment you pass, it will look to you as if that car is moving backwards (try it next time you're in the car and not driving!). The car is not actually moving backwards, it just looks that way. In Figure 4.7, Mars is in prograde motion from dots 1 to 3, retrograde motion from dots 3 to 5, and prograde motion again from dots 5 to 7.

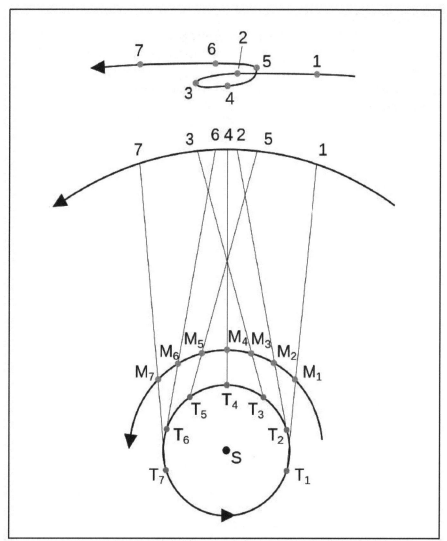

Figure 4.7: Copernicus' Model of the Solar System Explains Retrograde Motion
(https://commons.wikimedia.org/wiki/File:Qualitative_apparent_retrograd_motion_of_Mars_top-down.svg)

In science, when there is more than one hypothesis that correctly explains the data, the one that is simpler and makes less assumptions often turns out to be the correct one (this is known as Occam's Razor). This example is no exception; though it took some time for the Earth-centered model to lose its hold, Copernicus' sun centered model eventually won out!

Questions You Should Be Able to Answer
10. Why did ancient astronomers believe that the Earth was the center of the solar system and that the Earth doesn't move?
11. What do we mean by the "retrograde motion" of the planets?
12. Describe Ptolemy's model of the solar system. How did this model explain retrograde motion?
13. Describe Copernicus' model of the solar system. How did this model explain retrograde motion?

Suggestions for Further Reading

3. http://www.lasalle.edu/~smithsc/Astronomy/retrograd.html (explanation of retrograde motion)
4. http://astro.unl.edu/classaction/animations/renaissance/marsorbit.html (Ptolemy's model retrograde motion animation)
5. http://astro.unl.edu/classaction/animations/renaissance/retrograde.html (Copernicus' model retrograde motion animation)

Chapter 4 Activity: Models of the S`olar System

Part 1: Ptolemy's Model

Because the Sun and planets appear to move around the Earth, early astronomers assumed that that the Earth was at the center of the solar system and that the planets orbited in circles around the Earth. However, this posed a problem in explaining retrograde motion. We will illustrate this problem.

The image below shows the orbit of Mars around the Earth in an Earth-centered model of the solar system. Mars' location for 5 months is shown. The top part of the image illustrates the background stars as seen from Earth; please note that east is to the left and west is to the right in this image.

Instructions: Draw lines connecting the Earth and Mars at each location and extend the lines to the background stars. This represents where Mars would appear in the sky to an Earth observer; draw Mars as it would appear in the sky and label the month. March (3) has been done for you as an example. Then answer the questions below.

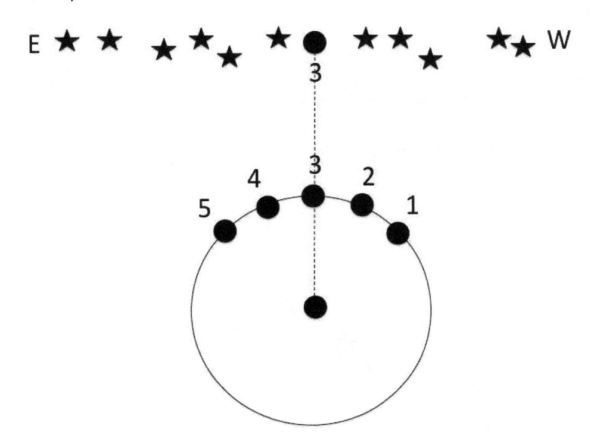

1. Describe how Mars appears to move in the sky from January to May (E to W or W to E)?

2. During what times from January to May is Mars in prograde motion? During what times from January to May is Mars in retrograde motion?

3. Can the simple Earth-centered model of the solar system shown above explain the apparent retrograde motion of the planets in the sky? Why or why not?

In response to the problem above, the Greek astronomer Ptolemy created a new Earth-centered model of the solar system (AD 140). Instead of having the planets orbit directly around the Earth, he had the planets orbit around small circles (epicycles), which simultaneously orbited the Earth. The image below shows the orbit of Mars around the Earth in Ptolemy's model. Mars' location for 7 months is shown.

Instructions: Draw lines connecting the Earth and Mars at each location and extend the lines to the background stars. Draw Mars as it would appear in the sky and label the month. February (2) has been done for you as an example. Then answer the questions below.

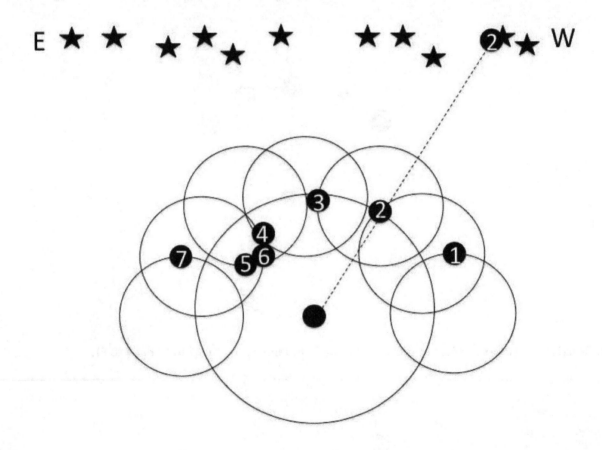

4. Describe how Mars appears to move in the sky from January to July (E to W or W to E)?

5. During what times from January to July is Mars in prograde motion? During what times from January to July is Mars in retrograde motion?

6. Can Ptolemy's model of the solar system shown above explain the apparent retrograde motion of the planets in the sky? Why or why not?

Polish astronomer Copernicus realized an alternative way to solve the retrograde motion problem: he created a Sun-centered model of the solar system (1543). In this model, all of the planets (including the Earth) orbit the Sun. The image below shows the orbits of Earth and Mars around the Sun in Copernicus' model (Earth is the smaller orbit, Mars is the larger obit). Earth's and Mars' locations for 5 months is shown.

Instructions: Draw lines connecting the Earth and Mars at each location and extend the lines to the background stars. Draw Mars as it would appear in the sky and label the month. January (1) has been done for you as an example. Then answer the questions below.

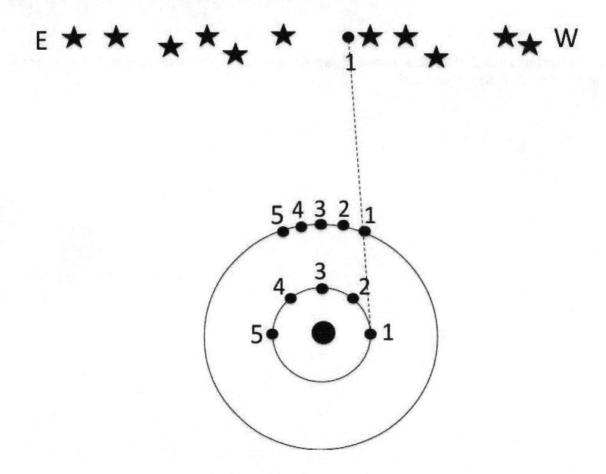

7. Describe how Mars appears to move in the sky from January to May (E to W or W to E)?

8. During what times from January to May is Mars in prograde motion? During what times from January to July is Mars in retrograde motion?

9. Can Copernicus model of the solar system shown above explain the apparent retrograde motion of the planets in the sky? Why or why not?

10. Explain in one sentence how Ptolemy's model explains the apparent retrograde motion of the planets. Then explain in one sentence how Copernicus' model explains the apparent retrograde motion of the planets.

11. In science when two hypotheses both adequately explain the same data, we generally choose the one that makes the fewest assumptions (this is known as Occum's razor). Given this information, do you think Ptolemy's or Copernicus' model of the solar system makes the most sense?

In this chapter, we will continue to discuss how scientists developed an accurate model of the solar system. You will learn about Kepler's three laws of motion, which can be used to accurately describe planetary motions.

In the mid to late 1500s, a gentleman named Tycho Brahe set out to create the most mathematically accurate model of the solar system to date. To help him, he hired an assistant, Johannes Kepler. Unfortunately, Brahe held strongly to an Earth-centered view of the solar system, and began to create his model in the style of Ptolemy, with many epicycles. However, Brahe died before the model was complete, leaving Kepler to finish. Kepler then abandoned the Earth-centered view in favor of the Sun-centered view. In doing so, Kepler realized that three laws can describe the motions of the planets. We now call these laws "Kepler's Laws of Planetary Motion."

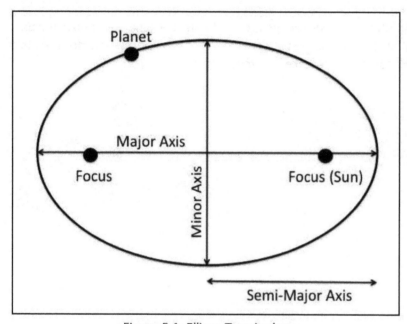

Figure 5.1: Ellipse Terminology

Kepler's 1st Law states that the planets orbit the Sun in ellipses with the Sun at one focus. This means that the planets' orbits are not perfectly circular; they are in fact slightly oval. Figure 5.1 illustrates some important terminology. Just as a circle has a center, an ellipse has two foci. The Sun is at one focus; the other focus is empty. The long axis of the ellipse is known as the major axis, and the short axis is known as the minor axis. Half of the major axis is the semi-major axis. This is important because it is mathematically equivalent to the planet's average distance from the Sun. Note that any point on the ellipse has some distance to the Sun and some distance to the empty focus. An ellipse is defined so that that sum of these distances is always the same, no matter where on the ellipse you are. An ellipse can be more oval or less oval; we describe the degree of ovalness with the eccentricity, which is a decimal in between 0 and 1. An eccentricity of 0 represents a perfect circle, and an eccentricity of 1 represents a straight line. Figure 5.2 shows examples of ellipses with different eccentricities. When the eccentricity is 0, the two foci are

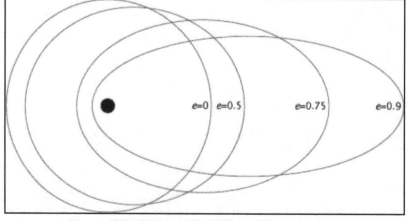

Figure 5.2: Ellipses With Different Eccentricities, Same Semi-Major Axis (http://nasa.gov)

at the same place and we have a perfect circle. As the eccentricity increase, the foci move further and further apart, and the ellipse becomes more and more oval.

Kepler's 2nd Law states that a line from a planet to the Sun sweeps over equal areas in equal intervals of time. The example in Figure 5.3 illustrates this. Note that Area A_1 = Area A_2 = Area A_3; the amount of shading is the same. Thus the planet takes the same amount of time to cover the distance represented by Area A_1, the distance represented by Area A_2, and so forth. Note also that though the areas are the same, *the distances are not the same*! The distance closer to the Sun (e.g. the distance corresponding to Area A_3), is in fact longer than the distance further from the Sun (e.g. the distance corresponding to Area A_1). This means that when the planet is closer to the Sun, it has to cover a greater distance in the same amount of time. In order to do this, it must be traveling faster.

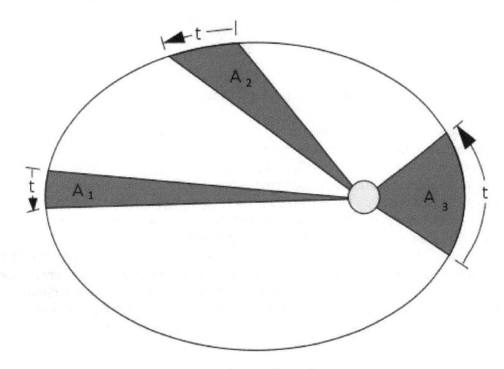

Figure 5.3: Kepler's 2nd Law Illustration
(https://commons.wikimedia.org/wiki/File:Kepler%27s_law_2_ru.svg)

Thus a consequence of Kepler's 2nd Law is that the speed a planet travels during its orbit changes and is related to its distance from the Sun. When the planet is closer to the Sun it travels faster, and when the planet is further from the Sun, it travels slower. Thus the planet's slowest speed will be at the furthest point from the Sun, and the fastest speed will be at the closest point to Sun (Figure 5.4). As the planet gets closer to the Sun it will speed up, and as it gets further from the Sun it will slow down. So in diagram 5.4 if the planet is traveling counterclockwise, all along the top half of the orbit shown it will be slowing down (at the points on the orbit marked by Xs) and all along the bottom half of the orbit shown it will be speeding up (at the points on the orbit marked by asterisks). Note: be careful not to confuse how fast the planet is moving with whether or not it is speeding up or slowing down! The speed is determined by the distance; whether it is speeding up or slowing down is determined by whether it is currently moving away or towards the Sun. For example, consider the X closest to the fastest point and the asterisk closest to the fastest point. Both are the same distance from the Sun, so at both points the planet is traveling the same speed (which is pretty fast since it is close to the Sun). However, at the asterisk the planet is speeding up (think of a car going 60 mph where you are stepping on the gas) and at the X the planet is slowing down (think of a car going 60 mph where you are stepping on the breaks).

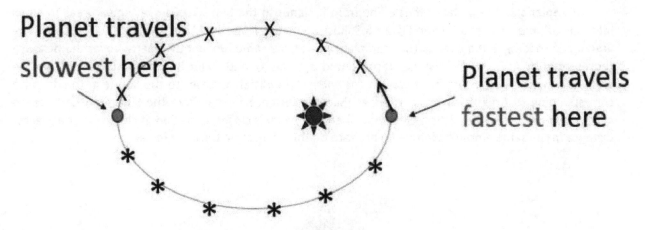

Figure 5.4: Variation in Planet Speed During Orbit

Lastly is Kepler's 3rd Law. This law tells us that a planet's orbital period squared is proportional to its semi-major axis cubed. In mathematical form, this is $p^2 = a^3$. p is the period in years; it is how long the planet takes to orbit the Sun once. The Earth's period, for example, is one year. a is the semi-major axis in AU; this is the planet's average distance from the Sun. The Earth's semi-major axis, for example, is 1 AU. Note that p^2 means the period times itself, and that a^3 means the semi-major axis times itself times itself again. In words, what the third law means is that planets that are closer to the Sun have shorter orbital periods (because they travel faster and have less distance to go) and planets that are further from the Sun have longer orbital periods (because they travel slower and have more distance to go). For example, in Figure 5.5(A) there are two planets orbiting the Sun, a big one and a small one. Since the big one is further away, it has a longer period. In Figure 5.5(B) both planets are the same distance from the Sun, so they have the same period. Note that the fact that one planet is bigger than the other is irrelevant. Kepler's 3rd Law tells us that the only factor that matters in determining the period is distance.

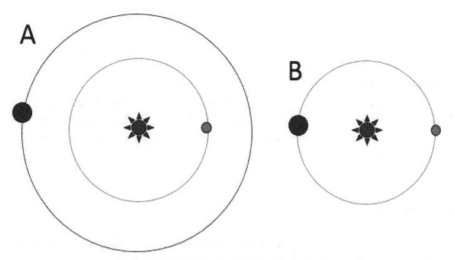

Figure 5.5: Kepler's 3rd Law Example

Figure 5.6 demonstrates Kepler's 3rd Law for the solar system. For each planet, the period and semi-major axis are listed. The fourth column shows the period squared, and the last column shows the semimajor axis cubed. Note that the last two columns are equal (within rounding error), in accordance with the third law.

	Period P (years)	Semi-major Axis a (AU)	P^2	a^3
Mercury	0.24	0.39	0.058	0.059
Venus	0.61	0.72	0.372	0.373
Earth	1	1	1.000	1.000
Mars	1.88	1.52	3.534	3.512
Jupiter	11.86	5.2	140.660	140.608
Saturn	29.46	9.54	867.892	868.251
Uranus	84.01	19.19	7057.680	7066.835
Neptune	164.79	30.06	27155.744	27162.324

Figure 5.6: Demonstration of Kepler's Third Law

Questions You Should Be Able to Answer
1. What are Kepler's Three Laws?

Suggestions for Further Reading
1. http://astro.unl.edu/naap/pos/pos_background1.html (explanation of Kepler's Laws)
2. http://www.astro.washington.edu/users/smith/Astro150/Tutorials/Kepler/ (another explanation of Kepler's Laws)

Suggestions for Practice
3. http://astro.unl.edu/interactives/kepler/KeplerFirstLaw.html (1st Law Questions)
4. http://astro.unl.edu/interactives/kepler/KeplerSecondLaw.html (2nd Law Questions)
5. http://astro.unl.edu/interactives/kepler/KeplerThirdLaw.html (3rd Law Questions)
6. http://astro.unl.edu/classaction/questions/renaissance/ca_renaissance_kepler2nd.html (more 2nd Law Questions)

Common Pitfalls

-Be sure not to confuse the 2nd and 3rd laws. Both deal with speed, but they refer to different things. The 2nd law tells us what a *particular* planet does as it orbits the Sun; when it is closer to the Sun it moves faster. The 3rd law compares the orbital periods for *all* of the planets in the solar system; planets that are further from the Sun travel slower and have longer orbital periods.

-When thinking about the 2nd law, don't confuse area and distance; they are different. Area is how much space something (in this case the space that the line connecting the planet to the sun) sweeps out. Distance is how long a line is. For example, the two rectangles below have the same area even though the rectangle on the right has a much longer side.

Chapter 5 Activity: Kepler's Laws of Planetary Motion

Part 1: Kepler's 1st Law

1. Circle the correct choices from the italicized options: Kepler's 1st Law says that planets orbit the Sun in ***perfect circles / ellipses***. The degree of ovalness of an orbit is given with the eccentricity, which is a decimal ranging from 0 to 1. The eccentricity of a perfect circle is ***0 / 1***, and the larger the eccentricity, the ***more circular / more oval*** the orbit.

2. The table below lists the eccentricities of some imaginary planets. Rank the planets' orbits from most circular to most oval.

Planet	Eccentricity
Planet W	0.021
Planet X	0.0007
Planet Y	0.005
Planet Z	0.0

The diagram below shows the orbit of 4 planets around the Sun (solid black lines). The dashed gray lines are evenly spaced circles around the Sun for reference.

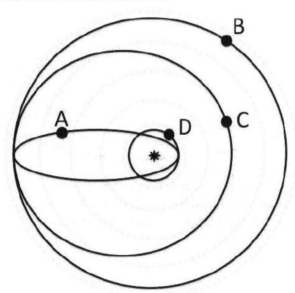

3. Rank the planet's orbits from least eccentric to most eccentric. If any are equal, use an equal sign.

4. Rank the planet's semi-major axes from furthest to closest. If any are equal, use an equal sign.

Part 2: Kepler's 2nd Law

5. Circle the correct choices from the italicized options: Kepler's 2nd Law says that a line connecting the planet to the Sun covers over equal *areas / distances* in the same amount of time. As a result of the 2nd Law, a planet travels *faster / slower* when it is closer to the Sun and *faster / slower* when it is further from the Sun.

The diagram below shows the orbit of a planet around the Sun. 8 locations in the orbit are marked. Question 6-14 refer to this diagram.

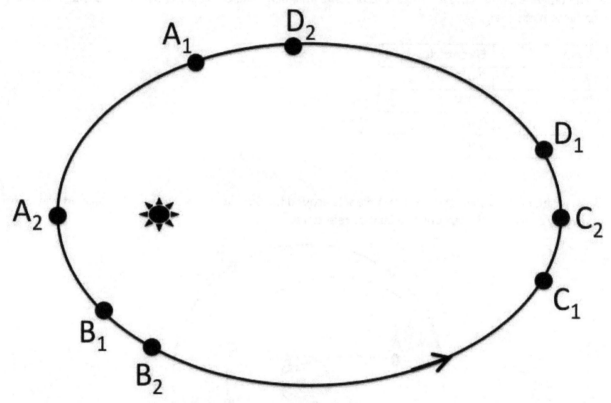

6. Draw a line connecting the planet at position A_1 to the Sun. Then draw a line connecting the planet at position A_2 to the Sun. Next shade in the resulting area ("area A"). This is the area that a line from the planet to the Sun sweeps out as the planet travels from point A_1 to point A_2.

7. Repeat step 7 to shade in areas B, C, and D.

8. Which pair of areas is the same?

9. Two students are discussing their answers to the previous question:

Student A says, "*I chose area B and area C because the distance from B_1 to B_2 looks about the same as the distance from C_1 to C_2.*"

Student B says, "*But area and distance are not the same thing. For example, a square that is 2 inches by 2 inches has the same area as a rectangle that is 4 inches by 1 inches (e.g. an area of 4 inches squared) even though the rectangle is longer. You have to pick the two areas that look like they have about the same amount of shading. So I picked A and C. Area D is much bigger and Area B is much smaller.*"

With which student(s) do you agree, and why (revise your answer to 8 if necessary)?

10. For the two areas you picked in question 8, how does the *time* it takes the planet to cover each area compare? Give a reasoning for your answer.

11. For the two areas you picked in question 8, how does the *distance* traveled as the planet covers each area compare? Give a reasoning for your answer.

12. For the two areas you picked in question 8, how does the *speed* of the planet as the planet covers each area compare? Give a reasoning for your answer.

13. At what lettered location is the planet traveling the fastest? At what lettered location is it traveling the slowest?

14. At which of the lettered locations is the planet speeding up? At which of the lettered locations is the planet slowing down?

15. The table below lists the eccentricities of some imaginary planets. Which planet will experience no change in speed as it orbits the Sun? Which planet will experience the biggest change in speed as it orbits the Sun?

Planet	Eccentricity
Planet W	0.021
Planet X	0.0007
Planet Y	0.005
Planet Z	0.0

Part 3: Kepler's 3rd Law

16. Circle the correct choices from the italicized options: Kepler's 3rd Law says a planet's orbital period depends on its *distance / mass / both mass and distance*. The further a planet is from the Sun, the *longer / shorter* the orbital period.

17. A student says, "I get how Kepler's 3rd Law works. Planets that are further from the Sun are bigger and as they get bigger they take longer to complete an orbit." How do you respond? Use the table below to provide support for your answer.

	Period P (years)	Semi-major Axis a (AU)	Mass (in terms of Earth's mass)
Mercury	0.24	0.39	0.0552
Venus	0.61	0.72	0.815
Earth	1	1	1.000
Mars	1.88	1.52	0.107
Jupiter	11.86	5.2	317.8
Saturn	29.46	9.54	95.2
Uranus	84.01	19.19	14.5
Neptune	164.79	30.06	17.1

18. Suppose that you move a planet closer to the Sun. What would happen to its orbital period (choose one)?

a. it would increase

   b. it would decrease

   c. it would stay the same

19. Suppose that you make a planet bigger. What would happen to its orbital period (choose one)?

a. it would increase

   b. it would decrease

   c. it would stay the same

20. Rank the planets below from longest to shortest orbital period. If any are equal, use an equal sign.

Planet	Mass (in terms of Earth Masses)	Semi-Major Axis	Eccentricity
Planet W	14	0.5 AU	0.021
Planet X	20	2 AU	0.0007
Planet Y	20	3.5 AU	0.005
Planet Z	25	2 AU	0.0

Chapter 6: Seasons

In this chapter, you will learn why we experience seasons.

The Earth is constantly moving. It rotates on its axis once a day, and it revolves around the Sun once a year.

The rotation of the Earth causes night and day. When you are on the side of the Earth that is facing the Sun, it is daytime. When you are on the side of the Earth facing away from the Sun, it is nighttime. Figure 6.1 shows the Earth's rotation as seen looking down on the north pole. The arrows represent the direction that the sunlight is coming from (the Sun is to the right in this diagram). Seen this way, the Earth rotates counterclockwise, and different times of day correspond to different positions in the rotation. For example, when you are directly facing the Sun it is noon, and when you are directly facing away from the Sun, it is midnight. When you are moving from the lit half of the Earth to the unlit half, it is sunset (about 6 pm), and when you are moving from the unlit half to the lit half, it is sunrise (about 6 am).

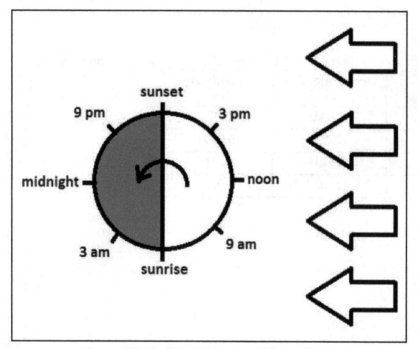

Figure 6.1: Earth's Rotation and Time of Day

The revolution of the Earth causes the seasons. There is a common misconception that this is a result of the Earth's elliptical orbit. A lot of people believe that we have seasons because we are closer to the Sun in the summer and further from the Sun in the winter. This is NOT true.

Remember the Earth's orbit to scale; it is almost a circle (Figure 6.2)! The ellipticity is not enough to cause significant temperature differences. While the distance between the Earth and the Sun does vary by 5 million km, this is a difference of only about 3% of the average Earth-Sun distance...essentially insignificant. In fact, if you look at the distance between the Earth and Sun (Figure 6.2), we are actually closer to the Sun in December, when we experience winter. Furthermore, when it is summer for us, it is actually winter for the southern hemisphere. The southern hemisphere experiences opposite seasons from us. This would not be the case if the Earth's elliptical orbit were what caused the seasons. If the elliptical orbit were what caused the seasons, both hemispheres would experience summer at the same time (when the Earth was closest to the Sun).

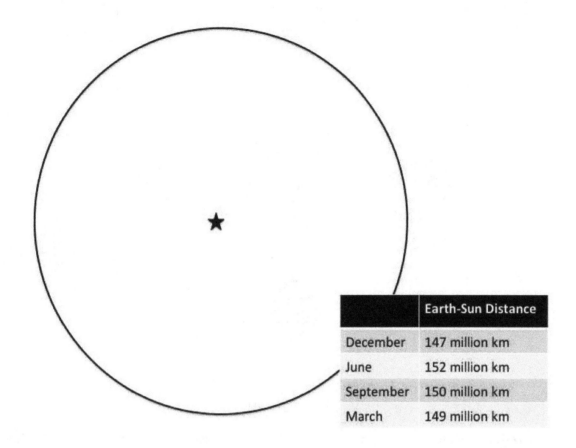

	Earth-Sun Distance
December	147 million km
June	152 million km
September	150 million km
March	149 million km

Figure 6.2: The Earth's Orbit to Scale

So what does cause the seasons? The answer is the Earth's tilt. The Earth's rotational axis is tilted 23.5 degrees from vertical. The direction and amount of tilt always remains the same (e.g. no matter what time of year, the axis is always tilted 23.5 degrees towards the same direction in space), but because the Earth revolves around the Sun, this means that at different times of year different parts of the Earth are tilted towards and away from the Sun (Figure 6.3). In June, the northern hemisphere is tilted towards the Sun and we experience summer while the southern hemisphere experiences winter. In December, the southern hemisphere is tilted towards the Sun and we experience winter while the southern hemisphere experiences summer. In spring and fall, neither hemisphere is tilted towards the Sun.

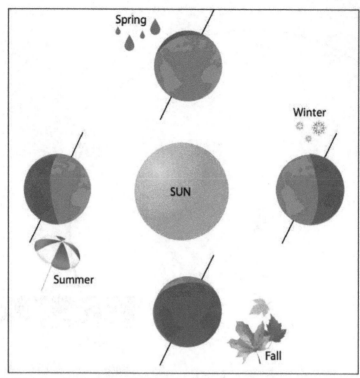

Figure 6.3: Seasons and the Earth's Tilt – Seasons Given for Northern Hemisphere
(http://www.nasa.gov)

Why does the tilt matter? The tilt matters for two reasons. The first is the concentration of sunlight. When we are tilted towards the Sun, the Sun gets higher in the sky and the sunlight we receive is more concentrated (this is known as direct sunlight). When we are tilted away from the Sun, the Sun remains lower in the sky and the sunlight we receive is less concentrated (this is known as indirect sunlight).

This concept is illustrated in Figure 6.4. The line running across the Earth is the equator, and the dot halfway between the equator and the North Pole represents our location (NY). Note that in summer, the same beam of sunlight (represented by the flashlight) is spread out over less area than in the winter. Since it is spread out over a smaller area, it is more concentrated and it gets warmer.

Now also look at a location on the equator (the dot on the equator; Figure 6.5). Note that for the location on the

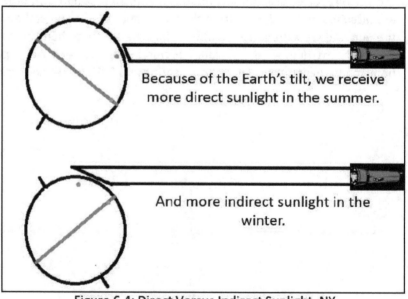

Because of the Earth's tilt, we receive more direct sunlight in the summer.

And more indirect sunlight in the winter.

Figure 6.4: Direct Versus Indirect Sunlight, NY

equator, there is not much difference in sunlight concentration between different times of the year...the sunlight is always concentrated and direct. This is why locations on the equator do not experience seasons; they are always warm. The further you go towards the poles, the more drastic the difference in sunlight concentration is between winter and summer, and the more drastic the seasonal change.

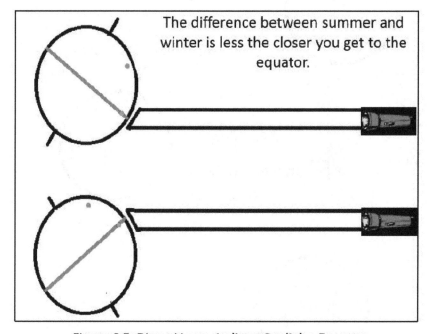

The difference between summer and winter is less the closer you get to the equator.

Figure 6.5: Direct Versus Indirect Sunlight, Equator

The second reason that the tilt matters is that it causes the number of daylight hours to vary (Figure 6.6). In June, the northern hemisphere gets proportionally more daylight hours (because it is tilted towards the Sun) and the southern hemisphere gets proportionally less (because it is tilted away from the Sun). The situation is reversed in December. So, for example, we (in NY, at 40 degrees north latitude) get about 15 hours of daylight in the summer, and 9 hours in the winter. In the spring and fall, everywhere on Earth gets the same amount of daylight (12 hours). Note that for the equator, the time of year once again does not matter; the equator always gets 12 hours of daylight. As you go towards the poles, the difference between summer and winter hours gets bigger. In fact, if you lived at the north or south poles, you would experience 6 months of daylight followed by 6 months of darkness! This is an additional reason why seasonal changes increase towards the poles and the equator does not experience seasons.

To sum up, when we are tilted towards the Sun we get more concentrated (direct) sunlight and more hours of sunlight. This makes it warmer and it is summer. When we are tilted away from the Sun we get less concentrated (indirect) sunlight and less hours of sunlight. This makes it colder and it is winter. Locations on the equator do not experience seasons because they always receive 12 hours of concentrated (direct) sunlight; they are always warm. Seasonal changes increase towards the poles.

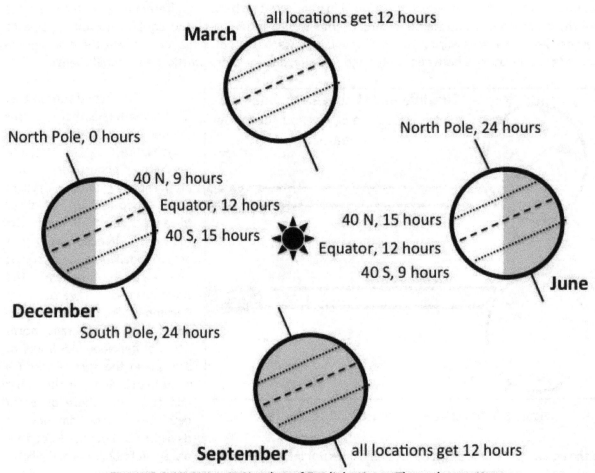

Figure 6.6: Variation in Number of Daylight Hours Throughout a Year

Questions You Should Be Able to Answer
1. Define rotation and revolution. How long does it take the Earth to complete a cycle of each?
2. What causes night and day?
3. What causes the seasons?

Suggestions for Further Reading
1. http://www.khanacademy.org/science/cosmology-and-astronomy/earth-history-topic/earth-title-topic/v/seasons-aren-t-dictated-by-closeness-to-sun (Khan Academy explanation of the seasons, part 1)
2. http://www.khanacademy.org/science/cosmology-and-astronomy/earth-history-topic/earth-title-topic/v/how-earth-s-tilt-causes-seasons (Khan Academy explanation of the seasons, part 2)
3. http://iqa.evergreenps.org/science/phy_science/tutorials/astrotutorials/Seasons/GoSeasons.html (seasons tutorial, plus practice questions)

Suggestions for Practice
4. http://astro.unl.edu/interactives/seasons/Season1_Distance.html (seasonal distance question)
5. http://astro.unl.edu/interactives/seasons/Season2_Flashlight.html (seasons direct/indirect light questions)
6. http://astro.unl.edu/interactives/seasons/Season3_illuminatedAreas.html (seasons illuminated areas questions)
7. http://astro.unl.edu/interactives/seasons/Season4_Time.html (seasons daylight time questions)

8. http://astro.unl.edu/interactives/seasons/Season5_Tilt.html (seasons tilt questions)

Common Pitfalls

-For many students the misconception that the seasons are caused by the varying distance from the Earth to the Sun is deeply ingrained. They try to reconcile this with their new knowledge that it is the tilt that causes the seasons by suggesting that when the Earth is tilted towards the Sun, it is summer because the tilt makes us closer. This is NOT true. The varying distance due to the tilt is far far less than the 5 million km difference due to the elliptical orbit. And if that 5 million km difference is too small to make a difference, the smaller distance difference do to the tilt is also far far too small to make a difference. Distance has in fact nothing to do with it! It is all about how the tilt changes the concentration and amount of light we receive.

-Remember that the Earth rotates! Many students will look at the diagram below and say the location marked with a star is experiencing winter because it is in the shaded portion. This is NOT true. The fact that the location marked with a star is in the shaded portion, just means it is nighttime because it is currently on the side of the Earth facing away from the Sun. 12 hours later, the Earth will have rotated and it will be daytime (the location marked by a star will follow the dashed path as the Earth rotates). Here, the location marked by a star is north of the equator (solid line), so it is in the northern hemisphere. The northern hemisphere is tilted towards the Sun, so it is summer.

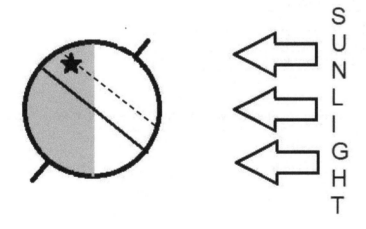

Chapter 6 Activity: Seasons

Part 1: Changing Distance Does Not Cause the Seasons

1. Which diagram below provides the best representation of the Earth's orbit around the Sun (circle one)?

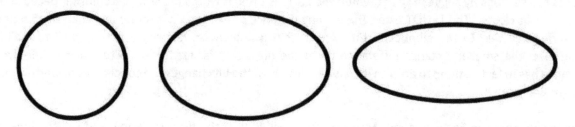

2. The table below shows the distance between the Earth and the Sun for different times of the year. During which month is the Earth closest to the Sun?

	Earth-Sun Distance
December	147 million km
June	152 million km
September	150 million km
March	149 million km

3. Does your answer to number 2 coincide with the time of year that your location experiences the warmest temperatures?

4. A student says, "I believe we have seasons because of the Earth's elliptical orbit. Because the orbit is elliptical, there are times of the year that we are closer to the Sun and times of the year that we are further from the Sun. When we are closer to the Sun, we receive more sunlight and it is summer. When we are further from the Sun, we receive less sunlight and it is winter." Cite at least two pieces of evidence to prove that this student is incorrect.

Part 2: Direct and Indirect Sunlight

The diagram below illustrates the direction of the Sun's light hitting the surface for two different times of the year (A and B) for our location in NY. A good analogy for the direction the light is hitting the surface is to think of a flashlight beam hitting the surface at different angles; this is also shown. Questions 5-10 refer to this diagram.

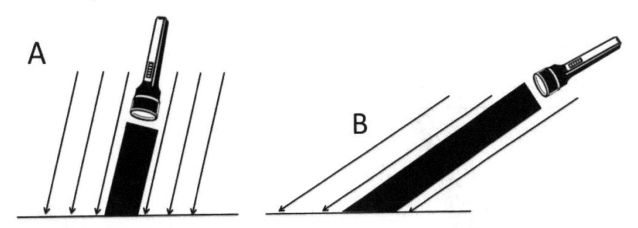

5. At which location is the Sun located higher in the sky, so that the rays are coming in closer to perpendicular with the surface (e.g. more directly)?

6. At which location is the beam of light from the flashlight spread out over a larger area?

7. Which lit up area from the flashlight would be brighter?

8. Suppose you place a thermometer under each flashlight beam. Which thermometer would read the higher temperature?

9. Label the appropriate diagrams with the words "more direct light" and the other diagram with the world "more indirect light."

10. Which diagram represents the way light hits the surface in the winter and which represents the way light hits the surface in the summer? Label the appropriate diagrams with the words "summer" and "winter."

11. The diagram previously represented our location in NY. The images below represent the variation in sunlight concentration throughout the year for two other locations: one location that is closer to the equator than our location (but still in the Northern Hemisphere) and one location that is closer to the North Pole than our location. Which is which? Label the diagram and explain your reasoning.

Part 3: Variation in Daylight Hours

The graph below shows the variation in daylight hours for New York City. Questions 12

12. When does NYC get the most hours of daylight? Approximately how many hours is this?

13. When does NYC get the least hours of daylight? Approximately how many hours is this?

14. NYC is at a latitude of 40.7 degrees N. On the plot, sketch what the sunlight curve would look like for a location that is at 40.7 degrees S. Label this "southern hemisphere."

15. On the plot, sketch what the sunlight curve would look like for a location that is on the equator. Label this "equator."

16. Describe how the curve would look different for a location that is more north of the equator than NYC (you don't have to draw this one).

Part 3: Putting it Together

17. Circle the correct choices from the italicized words:
The seasons *are / are not* caused by the changing distance of the Earth to the Sun. In fact, when we are closer to the Sun, it is *winter / summer* in the Northern Hemisphere. Instead, seasons are caused by the Earth's tilt. When the Northern Hemisphere is tilted towards the Sun, we receive more ***direct / indirect*** sunlight and ***more / less*** hours of sunlight. This makes it ***warmer / colder*** and it is ***summer / winter***. When the Northern Hemisphere is tilted away from the Sun, we receive more ***direct / indirect*** sunlight and ***more / less*** hours of sunlight. This makes it ***warmer / colder*** and it is ***summer / winter***. The Northern and Southern Hemispheres experience ***the same / opposite*** seasons at the same time. Locations near the equator experience ***little change / a lot of change*** in sunlight concentration and number of daylight hours with time, which is why the equator experiences little seasonal change.

In the diagram below, six planets are shown. The solid black lines represent the poles, and the dashed lines represent the equators. Letters mark off a location on each planet; assume that all of the locations are the same distance from the equator. Questions 18-23 refer to this diagram.

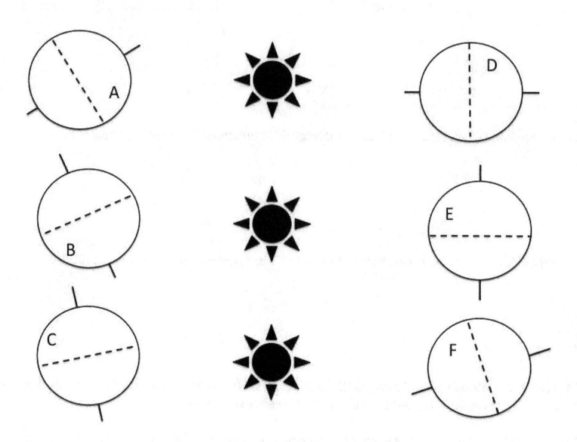

18. Which letters are experiencing summer?

19. Which letters are experiencing winter?

20. Which letters are experiencing fall or spring?

21. Which letters are experiencing daytime?

22. Which letters are experiencing nighttime?

23. Rank that letters in terms of number of daylight hours received from highest to lowest.

24. Rank the letters in terms of seasonal difference from greatest difference to least difference.

Chapter 7: Lunar Phases and Eclipses

In this chapter, you will learn why we see different phases of the moon and why we see eclipses.

You are probably aware that the moon goes through different shapes, or phases, over the course of a month. The moon starts completely dark. As the days progress, more and more of the moon becomes visible on the right-hand side until the moon is completely visible. Then the moon shrinks again, with the darkness coming in gradually from the right-hand side. Different moon phases have different names (Figure 7.1). If the moon is dark, this is known as a new moon. If the moon is completely lit, this is known as a full moon. When the moon is half lit, this is a quarter moon. If the half lit side is on the right, it is a 1st quarter, and if the half lit side is on the left, it is a third quarter. When the moon is between quarter and new, this is a crescent moon. If the lit up side is on the right, it is a waxing crescent moon. The term waxing means that the moon is getting bigger as time goes by. If the lit up side is on the left, it is a waning crescent moon. The term waning means that the moon is getting smaller as time goes by. When the moon is between quarter and full, this is a gibbous moon. If the lit up side is on the right, it is a waxing gibbous moon, and if the lit up side is on the left, it is a waning gibbous moon. (Note that things are slightly different in the southern hemisphere – in the southern hemisphere waxing and waning would be reversed, with waxing being when the moon was lit up on the left and waning being when the moon was lit up on the right!)

Figure 7.1: Moon Phases; Top Row → 1=new, 2=waxing crescent, 3=1st quarter, 4=waxing gibbous, 5=full
Bottom Row → 1=full, 2=waning gibbous, 3=3rd quarter, 4=waning crescent, 5=new
(https://commons.wikimedia.org/wiki/File:Waning_Moon_slides.jpg and
https://commons.wikimedia.org/wiki/File:Waxing_Moon_slides.jpg)

Figure 7.2 illustrates why we have moon phases. This shows the Earth-moon system looking down on the Earth's north pole. The moon's orbit around the Earth is shown (the inner circle represents the view that an alien would see looking down on the Earth's north pole, and the outer circle represents how someone on the Earth would see the moon). Note that the moon orbits counterclockwise around the

Earth, taking one month (or 4 weeks) to go around once. In this diagram, the Sun's light is coming from the right. Notice that the half of the moon facing the Sun is always lit up. However, we on Earth see the half of the moon that is facing us, which is not always the lit up half! The moon's position in its orbit around the Earth determines how much of the lit up half we see, and hence the phase. For example, when the moon is between the Earth and the Sun, the unlit side of the moon is facing the Earth. This corresponds to the new moon phase. Half a week later, a little sliver of lit up moon is visible on the right. This corresponds to the waxing crescent phase. As time continues, a greater and greater proportion of the lit up side is visible. When the moon reaches the opposite side of the Earth from the Sun (2 weeks after the new moon phase), the entire lit up side is facing the Earth, and this is the full moon phase. The next two weeks correspond to the moon getting smaller, going back to the new moon phase.

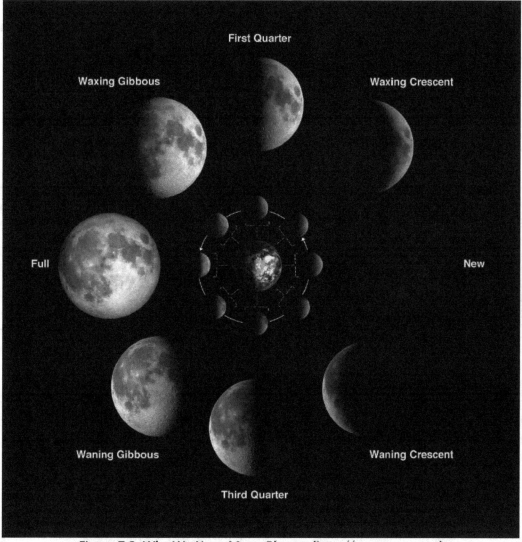

Figure 7.2: Why We Have Moon Phases (http://www.nasa.gov)

A lot of people assume that the moon is only visible during the night. However, if you think about it, you can probably think of a time when you saw the moon during the day! This is because different phases rise and set at different phases. However, a given phase will always rise and set at the same time. For example, the full moon will always rise at 6 pm and set at 6 am, and the waning crescent moon will always rise at 3 am and set at 3 pm.

Figure 7.3 shows an example to see how this works. In 7.3A, we have the Earth (middle), the moon (left), and the Sun coming from the right. Again, we are looking down on the Earth's north pole. The moon's position corresponds to a full moon phase, because the lit side of the moon is facing the Earth. Since the Earth rotates counterclockwise once every 24 hours, a viewer on the Earth will see the Sun at different positions in the sky. This corresponds to different times of day, which have been labeled.

In 7.3B, we see a viewer for whom it is noon. Note that I've blocked out the left hand half of the picture. That's because our viewer's horizon runs vertically down the middle of the page; the black is blocking out everything that is below the horizon and hence can't be seen at that time. Everything not blocked out is above the horizon and hence can be seen. For instance, here the Sun is directly overhead our viewer's head, at its highest point in the sky. Since our viewer is facing south, their left hand side is the eastern horizon (labeled E in the diagrams) and their right hand side is the western horizon (labeled W in the diagrams). Note that the moon is below the horizon. So while the moon is still there, and is still full, it can't be seen at noon because it hasn't risen yet.

Let's move 3 hours ahead (7.3C). It is now 3 pm for our viewer. Notice that our viewer's view of the sky has changed a bit. A part of the sky which was below the horizon before is now visible. A part of the sky which was above the horizon before is now below and is not visible. The Sun is lower in our viewer's sky. However, the moon is still not yet visible. 7.3D moves ahead another 3 hours. It is now 6 pm, and the Sun is setting in the west. Notice what the full moon is doing. It is just starting to rise on the eastern horizon! 3 hours later, at 9 pm, the full moon is still visible, but it is higher in the sky than it was before (7.3E). At midnight, the full moon is now directly overhead, and has reached its highest position in the sky (7.3F). At 3 am, the full moon is still visible, but is lower in the sky (7.3G). At 6 am, we see the full moon setting in the west, and the Sun rising in the east (7.3H).

Figure 7.4 shows what this would look like if you were standing on the Earth facing south. Since you are facing south, east would be to your left and west would be to your right. At 6 pm, you would see the full moon rise on the eastern horizon (note that objects in the sky always rise in the east and set in the west). As the night progressed, it would rise higher and higher in the sky until midnight, when it would reach its highest position over the southern horizon. After that time, the moon would progressively get lower in the sky, until it sets at 6 am.

Now imagine another phase, like the waxing crescent phase, which would place the moon directly about the position corresponding to 3 pm on the Earth. It is clear that the waning crescent phase would be visible at 3 pm, even though the full moon would not be visible. Thus the position of the moon, and hence the phase, determines the rising and setting time!

Figure 7.3: Full Moon Location Throughout Day

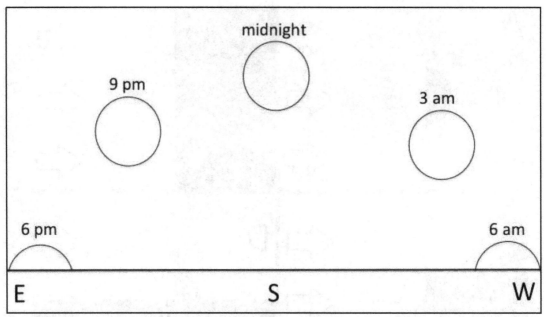

Figure 7.4: Full Moon's Position in Sky at Different Times

There is a simple way to determine rising and setting times. You can make a diagram as shown in Figure 7.5, showing the Earth and the times on the Earth, and the different phases of the moon. Note that each phase is directly above a certain time on the Earth. This is the time that that phase appears highest in the sky. For example, the 3rd quarter phase is highest in the sky at 6 am and the waxing crescent phase is highest in the sky at 3 pm. Since the moon is above the horizon for 12 hours (half the day) you can then get the rising time by going backward (subtracting) 6 hours and the setting time by going forward (adding) 6 hours. Let's use the waxing gibbous phase an example. The waxing gibbous phase is highest in the sky at 9 pm. Thus is rises at 3 pm (6 hours earlier) and sets at 3 am (6 hours later).

When you are using Figure 7.5 to determine rising and setting times, remember that the time of day does *not* determine the phase. For example, just because it is 9 pm does not mean that it is a waxing gibbous phase. The phase of the moon does not change over a day; it takes about 3.5 days to go from one phase to another! Thus at 9 pm, the moon could be in any phase. The phase is determined by where the moon is in its orbit around the Earth; the time of day just determines whether or not you can see the moon and where in the sky you see it.

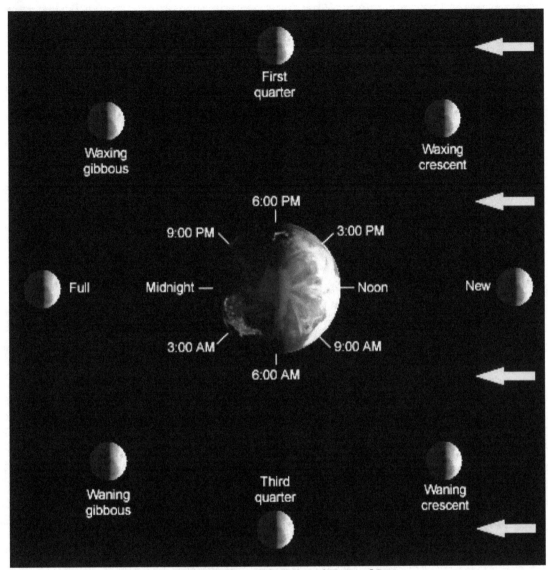

Figure 7.5: Moon Phases and Time of Day
(https://commons.wikimedia.org/wiki/File:Lunar-Phase-Diagram.png)

Before we finish with lunar phases, let's take a moment to talk about eclipses. There are two types of eclipses: lunar eclipses and solar eclipses. A lunar eclipse occurs when the moon passes through the Earth's shadow (Figure 7.6). Since the Earth's shadow falls behind the Earth, a lunar eclipse will only occur when the moon is full. What you will see during a lunar eclipse is the moon slowly getting darker as the Earth's shadow falls across it. When the moon is entirely within the Earth's shadow, it will actually appear red. This is from light being bent through the Earth's atmosphere and reflected off of the moon. It looks red because red light is bent the most. Note that if there is a lunar eclipse, every location on the Earth that is having nighttime when the eclipse occurs will see it.

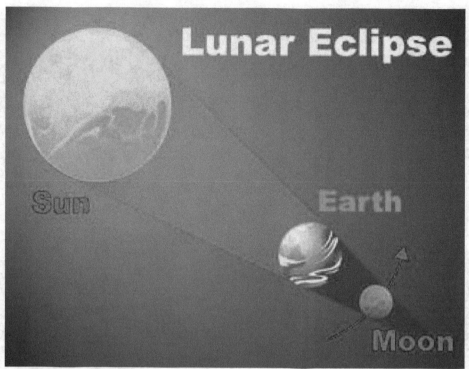

Figure 7.5: Configuration During A Lunar Eclipse (http://www.nasa.gov)

A solar eclipse occurs when the new moon passes between the Earth and the Sun and blocks the light from the Sun, casting a shadow on the Earth (Figure 7.6). Since the shadow only falls on a small portion of the Earth, you need to be within a narrow swath about 100 miles wide to see the eclipse. An interesting coincidence is that the Sun and the moon appear the same size in the Earth's sky. Remember the Sun is *actually* about 400 times bigger than the moon – but because it is so much further away, it appears the same size! This means that during a solar eclipse, the moon will exactly cover the Sun, making it completely dark (like nighttime) and leaving just the glow from the Sun's outermost layers visible (Figure 7.7).

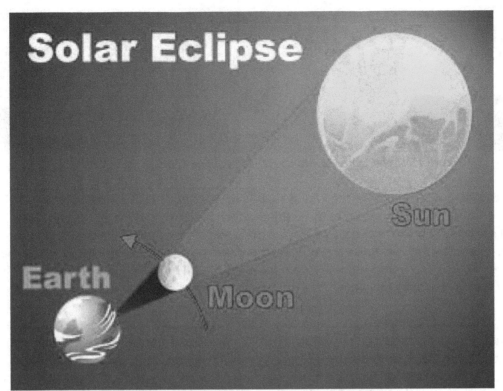

Figure 7.5: Configuration During A Solar Eclipse

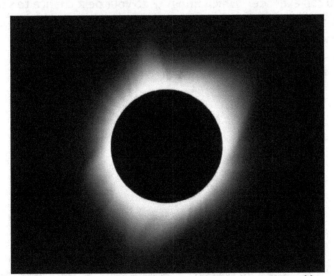

Figure 7.6: Sun/Moon During a Solar Eclipse, 2017 Eclipse (http://www.nasa.gov)

This is not true for every planet! For example Figure 7.7 shows views from a solar eclipse as viewed from Mars; the Martian moon Phobos is eclipsing the Sun, but it is not as big as the Sun in the Martian sky. These photos were taken by the rover Curiosity on the surface of Mars.

Figure 7.7: Solar Eclipse from the Surface of Mars (http://www.nasa.gov)

You might now be wondering why we don't have eclipses every month. This is because the Moon's orbit is slightly tilted relative to the plane between the Earth and the Sun (Figure 7.8). So usually the Earth's shadow falls above or below the full moon and the new moon's shadow falls above or below the Earth. There are only two times a year when the shadows are potentially aligned. If the moon is full during one of these two times, there will be a lunar eclipse. If the moon is new, there will be a solar eclipse. If the moon is any other phase, there will be either no eclipse or a partial eclipse.

Figure 7.9 shows recent upcoming total solar eclipses. In this time span, two fall across the continental US. The first occurred on August 21, 2017. Because it was the first total solar eclipse in the continental US since 1979, and because it covered an area ranging from coast to coast, it was nicknamed "The Great American Eclipse." Your professor was lucky enough to travel to Grand Teton National Park to view the eclipse from the region of totality (Figure 7.10), and can attest to the fact that it is one of the most amazing things you can ever see! Which brings us to your next chance to see a total solar eclipse in the US – which is on April 8, 2024. The region of totality for this eclipse will pass through portions of Texas, Oklahoma, Arkansas, Missouri, Illinois, Kentucky, Indiana, Michigan, Ohio, Pennsylvania, Vermont, New Hampshire, Maine, and even (a very very tiny portion near Buffalo) New York. Your next chance in the US after that will not be until 2044!

Figure 7.9: Upcoming Solar Eclipses (http://www.nasa.gov)

Figure 7.10: Your Professor Views the "Great American Eclipse" of 2017

Questions You Should Be Able to Answer
14. What causes lunar eclipses?
15. Given the position of the moon, Earth, and Sun, indicate the phase of the moon.
16. For each lunar phase, give the time that the phase rises, is highest in the sky, and sets.
17. What causes a lunar eclipse? What phase is the moon in during a lunar eclipse?
18. What causes a solar eclipse? What phase is the moon in during a solar eclipse?
19. Why don't lunar and solar eclipses happen every month?

Suggestions for Further Reading
6. http://astro.unl.edu/naap/lps/lunarPage1.html (moon phases explanation)
7. http://astro.unl.edu/classaction/animations/lunarcycles/lunarapplet.html (moon phases simulator)
8. http://iqa.evergreenps.org/science/phy_science/tutorials/astrotutorials/MoonPhases/GoMoon Phases.html (moon phases tutorial, plus practice questions)

Suggestions for Practice
9. http://astro.unl.edu/interactives/lunar/PercentOfIllumination.html (percent illumination questions)
10. http://astro.unl.edu/interactives/lunar/PhaseOrder.html (phase order questions)
11. http://astro.unl.edu/interactives/lunar/PhaseOrder_GeometricView.html (more phase order questions)
12. http://astro.unl.edu/interactives/lunar/PhaseOrder_MultipleViews.html (more phase order questions)
13. http://astro.unl.edu/interactives/lunar/EarthTimes.html (Earth times questions)
14. http://astro.unl.edu/interactives/lunar/EarthTimes3D.html (Earth times 3D questions)
15. http://astro.unl.edu/interactives/lunar/MeridianTimes.html (meridian times questions)
16. http://astro.unl.edu/interactives/lunar/RisingSettingTimes.html (rising and setting times questions)
17. http://astro.unl.edu/interactives/lunar/Flat_Horizon_View_SamePhase.html (horizon view questions)
18. http://astro.unl.edu/interactives/lunar/Flat_Horizon_View_sameStartTime.html (more horizon view questions)
19. http://astro.unl.edu/interactives/lunar/Flat_Horizon_View_AllDifferences.html (more horizon view questions)
20. http://astro.unl.edu/interactives/lunar/PhaseOrder_3DSunFixed.html (3D questions)
21. http://astro.unl.edu/interactives/lunar/PhaseOrder_3DSunVariable.html (more 3D questions)
22. http://astro.unl.edu/interactives/lunar/Lunar1_ST.html (sorting question 1)
23. http://astro.unl.edu/interactives/lunar/Lunar2_ST.html (sorting question 2)
24. http://astro.unl.edu/interactives/lunar/Lunar3_ST.html (sorting question 3)
25. http://astro.unl.edu/classaction/questions/lunarcycles/ca_lunarcycles_idphase.html (phase ID picture questions)
26. http://astro.unl.edu/classaction/questions/lunarcycles/ca_lunarcycles_idlunarpos.html (phase ID position questions)
27. http://astro.unl.edu/classaction/questions/lunarcycles/ca_lunarcycles_horzdiagidphase.html (phase ID horizon diagram questions)
28. http://astro.unl.edu/classaction/questions/lunarcycles/ca_lunarcycles_horzdiagidtime.html (time ID questions)

Common Pitfalls

-Fig. 7.5 does not imply that the moon is a waxing crescent at 3 pm, a first quarter at 6 pm, and so forth. Remember...the phase of the moon does not change over a single day. Fig. 7.5 just shows the times of day that each phase will appear highest in the sky; it does NOT mean that that is the only phase you can see at that time. For example, at 6 pm you could see any of the following phases: new (if it were visible), waxing crescent, first quarter, waxing gibbous, or full. All of these phases are above the horizon (or on the horizon, rising or setting) at the time. However, the only phase that will be at its highest position at that time is the first quarter phase; the other phases will appear elsewhere in the sky.

Chapter 7 Activity: Cause of Moon Phases

Part 1: Moon Phases

Questions 1-5 refer to the diagram below.

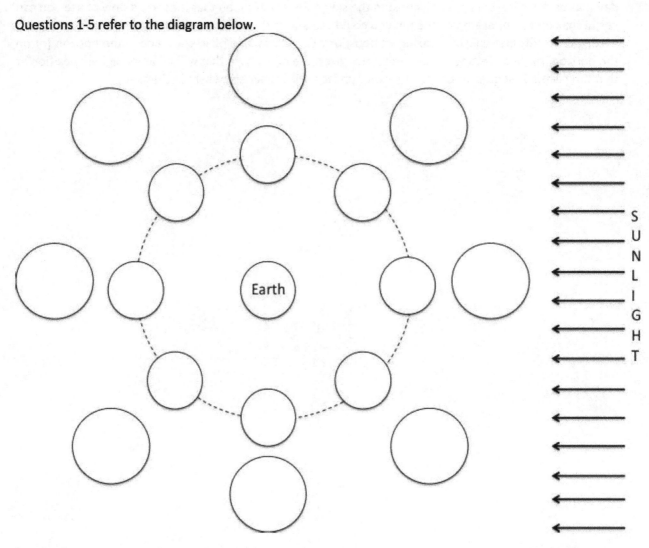

1. The diagram above shows a viewpoint of the Earth–Moon system looking down on the Earth's north pole. From this viewpoint, the moon orbits counterclockwise around the Earth. The inner circle in the diagram shows the position of the moon at different points in its orbit around the Earth. Imagine that you are alien looking down on the Earth-Moon system from this viewpoint. For each moon position in the inner circle, shade the portion of the moon that is NOT lit up by the Sun from this viewpoint.

2. Now imagine that you are standing on the Earth looking at the moon when it is at each position. In the outer circle, draw the phases of the moon that you would see from this viewpoint.

3. Write the appropriate name of each phase next to each diagram.

4. Rank the moon phases in terms of how much of the moon is lit up at each position from greatest to least. If any are equal, use an equals sign.

5. Rank the moon phases in terms of how much of the moon *that you see from Earth* is lit up at each position from greatest to least. If any are equal, use an equals sign.

6. The diagram below shows a student's explanation of why we have moon phases using a side-view of the Earth-Moon system. Do you agree with this explanation? Why or why not?

Earth's Shadow

New Moon

7. Two students are discussing their answers to the previous question:

Student A says, *"I agree with this diagram. We have moon phases because as the moon passes through the Earth's shadow, different amounts of the moon are lit up. So when the moon is entirely within the Earth shadow, as shown in the diagram, we see a new moon phase."*

Student B says, *"But I thought that a lunar eclipse was when the moon passes through the Earth's shadow. And that doesn't happen every month because the moon's orbit is tilted. So in the diagram shown the moon should be located either above or below the shadow and the entire surface will be lit up, meaning it is full moon."*

Student C says, *"I think you are really close. I agree that the orbit should be tilted and that the moon should be located either above or below the shadow. But it's not that the entire surface is lit up. Remember no matter where the moon is half of it will always be lit up because half of it is always facing the Sun. It is just that the moon's position in its orbit determines how much of the lit up half we see, and thus the phase. When the moon is behind the Earth the half that is lit up is facing the Earth, so that is why we see a full moon."*

With which student(s) do you agree, and why (revise your answer to 8 if necessary)?

8. In the diagram below, which shows a side view of the Earth-Moon system, redraw the moon's orbit to more accurately show why we have phases of the moon.

Part 2: Mars Phases

9. The diagram below shows the Sun, the orbit of the Earth, and the orbit of Mars. Four positions of Mars in its orbit are labeled. In the box below, draw what phase of Mars an observer on Earth would see when Mars is at each of the positions.

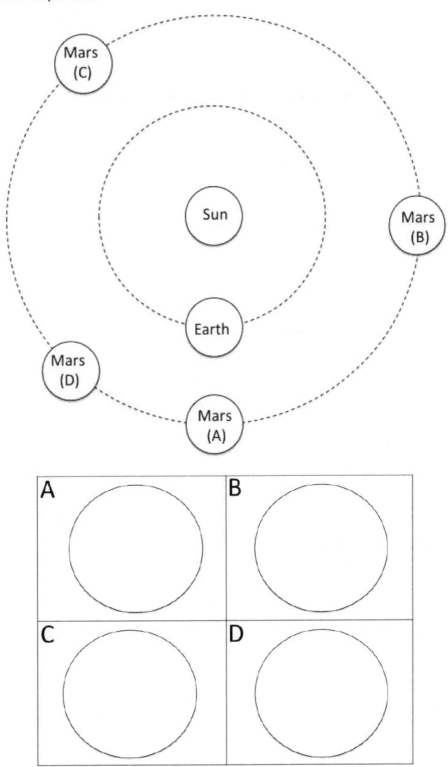

Chapter 7 Activity: Moon Phases Timing

For questions 1-6, assume that you are watching the full moon rise.

1. What time is it? Where should you look to see the moon rising?

2. What time will the moon set? What phase will the moon be when this happens? Where should you look to see the moon setting?

3. What phase will the moon be 3.5 days later?

4. What phase will the moon be one week later?

5. What phase will the moon be 3 weeks later?

6. 3 weeks later, what time will the moon rise?

The diagram below shows the Earth, the moon, and an observer on the Earth. The sunlight is coming from the right. Questions 7-12 refer to this diagram.

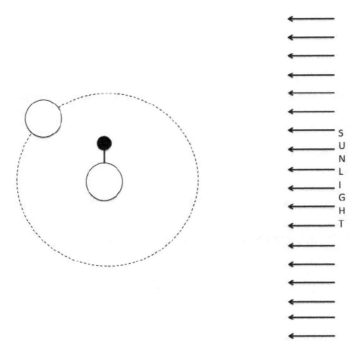

7. What time is it for the observer?

8. What moon phase does the observer see?

9. Draw where the observer will be 6 hours later. What moon phase will the observer see then?

10. What time will the moon shown appear to rise?

11. What time will the moon shown appear highest in the sky?

12. What time will the moon shown appear to set?

13. You see a moon in the sky at 3 pm. List all of the possible phases that this moon could be.

14. Your friend says that she saw an almost full moon in the early morning. Which phase did your friend see?

15. In the diagram below, draw where the waning crescent phase would be at noon.

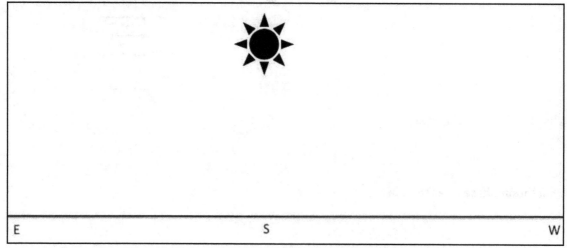

16. In the diagram in the previous question, what phase would the moon be in one week from then? Draw this phase in on the diagram where it would be at the same time shown (noon).

17. What is wrong with the diagram below?

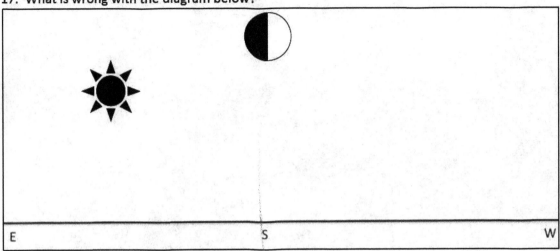

How did our solar system come to be?

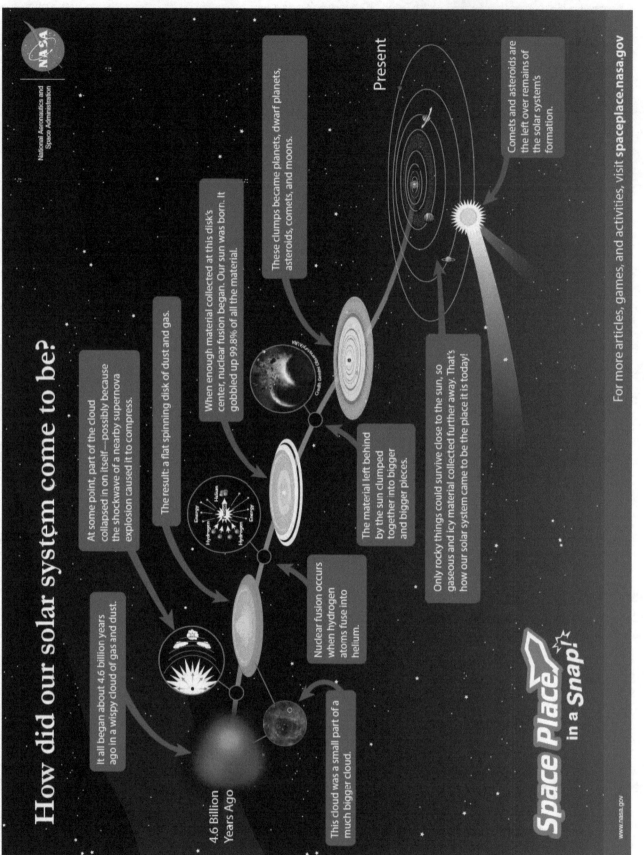

It all began about 4.6 billion years ago in a wispy cloud of gas and dust.

At some point, part of the cloud collapsed in on itself—possibly because the shockwave of a nearby supernova explosion caused it to compress.

The result: a flat spinning disk of dust and gas.

When enough material collected at this disk's center, nuclear fusion began. Our sun was born. It gobbled up 99.8% of all the material.

These clumps became planets, dwarf planets, asteroids, comets, and moons.

4.6 Billion Years Ago

This cloud was a small part of a much bigger cloud.

Nuclear fusion occurs when hydrogen atoms fuse into helium.

The material left behind by the sun clumped together into bigger and bigger pieces.

Only rocky things could survive close to the sun, so gaseous and icy material collected further away. That's how our solar system came to be the place it is today!

Present

Comets and asteroids are the left over remains of the solar system's formation.

National Aeronautics and Space Administration

Space Place. in a Snap!

www.nasa.gov

For more articles, games, and activities, visit **spaceplace.nasa.gov**

Chapter 8: Origin of the Solar System

In this chapter, you will learn about the prevailing hypothesis for the formation of the solar system, the solar nebula hypothesis. You will also learn about a process called differentiation and about the different types of atmospheres planets can have.

Recall that the Earth is one of eight planets in our solar system. Our Sun is one of hundreds of millions of stars in our galaxy, and our galaxy is one of hundreds of millions of galaxies in the universe. Here we are going to assume we have a galaxy and see how we go from a cloud of gas and dust in a galaxy into the solar system.

We are first going to see what observations scientists used when constructing a hypothesis for solar system formation. Any good model of solar system formation will need to explain these observations. I will then present the hypothesis, and in class we will discuss how these observations fit in with the hypothesis.

Our first observation is that all of the planets orbit the Sun in the same direction, in the same plane, and in nearly circular orbits. You can envision the solar system as a record with the Sun at the center and the planets moving counterclockwise around the center in the record grooves.

Not only do the planets orbit the Sun counterclockwise, but they also spin counterclockwise on their axes. The two exceptions are Uranus, which is tilted about 90 degrees on its axis, and Venus, which spins very slowly clockwise. Venus' spin is so slow that it takes 242 Earth days for it to rotate once!

Our third observation is that the planets can be divided into two groups, with the small rocky bodies (the Terrestrial planets) located close to the Sun and the large gaseous bodies (the Jovian planets) located far from the Sun.

Our final observation is that we have leftover debris in the solar system in the form of asteroids, KBOs, and comets.

These observations have led scientists to the prevailing hypothesis of planet formation, the solar nebular hypothesis. This hypothesis states that our solar system formed from the collapse of a large, spinning, spherical cloud of gas and dust.

This process is illustrated in Figure 8.1 (at end of chapter). The solar system begins as a large, spherical, spinning cloud of gas and dust. About 5 billion years ago, this cloud begins to collapse. Scientists believe that the shockwave from a nearby supernova explosion may have triggered the collapse. Just as an ice skater spins faster as she brings her arms closer to her body, the cloud spins faster as it collapses. As collapse continues, the cloud flattens out into a disk shape. Gravity causes most of the mass to concentrate in the center of the disk. As collapse proceeds, temperatures in the disk increase. Eventually temperatures in the center are hot enough that nuclear fusion begins and the Sun ignites. In the outer regions of the disk, small regions of matter start to collect and clump together. Nearer to the Sun, where temperatures are above boiling, these clumps include rock and metal. Further from the Sun, where temperatures are below freezing, these clumps also include different ices, like water ice, methane ice, and ammonia ice.   These small regions of collapsing matter grow into moon-sized protoplanets. The protoplanets grow into planets through collisions until most of the debris has been swept up. Because the outer regions of the solar system contain ice, the planets here grow faster and get so big that they are able to pull in gases (like hydrogen and helium) from the disk. Wind from the Sun eventually blows the remaining gas away from the newborn solar system. The timeline for solar system formation is roughly 100 million years.

Once formed, the early planets were very hot and mostly molten liquid. This is because of the heat generated by impacts during late stage planet formation as well as heat generated by short-lived radioactive isotopes that are no longer around.

Because the early planets were hot, this allowed a process called differentiation to occur. Differentiation is when a planet goes from being homogenous and well-mixed to being layered by density. To understand differentiation, imagine that you put some sand, water, and oil in a soda bottle, put a cap on the bottle, shake it up, and then set it down. The sand will sink to the bottom because it is heavier and the oil will rise to the top because it is lighter. The same thing happens with planets. The heavy material (the metal) will sink to the center, forming the core. The lighter material (the low density rock) will rise to the surface, forming the crust. The medium material (the medium density rock) will remain in the middle, forming the mantle.

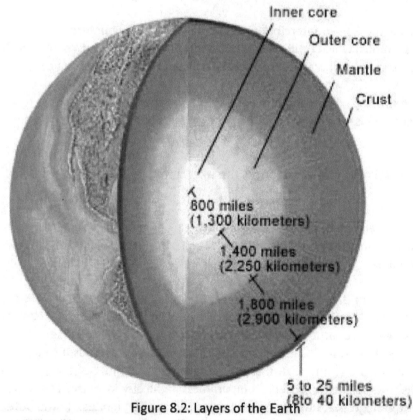

Figure 8.2 illustrates this for the Earth. The surface of the Earth is a layer of low-density rock named the crust. Note that this layer is very thin (only about 5 to 25 miles thick). To give you a sense of scale, the thickness of the crust relative to the whole Earth is about the same ratio as the thickness of an apple's skin relative to the whole apple! Underneath the crust is the mantle, which is made of high-density rock and is about 1,800 miles thick. At the center is the metallic core, which is the inner 2,200 miles. The core consists of two parts – the outer core is liquid and the inner core is solid.

Figure 8.2: Layers of the Earth
(https://commons.wikimedia.org/wiki/File:Earth_layers_NASA.png)

There are three different types of atmospheres that a planet can have. A primary atmosphere is one that is collected during planet formation and is composed primarily of hydrogen and helium. The Jovian planets have primary atmospheres; the Terrestrial planets don't because they didn't become big enough fast enough during planet formation to accumulate significant amounts of hydrogen and helium. An example of a primary atmosphere is Jupiter.

A secondary atmosphere is created from outgassing during differentiation. If you think back to the bottle of sand, water, and oil, and make the water carbonated, you will see an analogy to how this happens. If you shake up the mixture, take the cap off, and set the bottle down, as the sand sinks and the oil rises, the carbon dioxide will seep out. The same thing happened during planetary differentiation. Gases dissolved in the molten liquid seeped out, were held in by the planets' gravity, and became the secondary atmosphere. This gas was mostly carbon dioxide with some nitrogen. An example of a planet with a secondary atmosphere is Venus.

The Earth's early atmosphere looked a lot like Venus' atmosphere. However, the Earth's atmosphere underwent significant modification, or changes. Hence we call it a tertiary atmosphere. Much of the carbon dioxide in the Earth's atmosphere was removed as the Earth's oceans absorbed the carbon dioxide and stored it in rocks. Then oxygen was added as plants developed and emitted oxygen as part of photosynthesis. The result is that the Earth's atmosphere is composed of about 78% nitrogen and 21% oxygen, and is nearly 100 times thinner than Venus' atmosphere.

Questions You Should Be Able to Answer
1. What observations led to the solar nebula hypothesis?
2. Describe the Solar Nebula Hypothesis.
3. Why did some planets develop into terrestrial planets and some into Jovian planets?
4. Why were early planets hot?
5. What is differentiation?
6. What is the difference between a primary, secondary, and tertiary atmosphere? Where in the solar system can I find examples of each?

Suggestions for Further Reading
1. https://www.youtube.com/watch?v=Uhy1fucSRQI (Stephen Hawking explains the formation of the solar system in less than 5 minutes)
2. http://iqa.evergreenps.org/science/phy_science/tutorials/astrotutorials/SolSysForm/GoSolSysForm.html (solar system formation tutorial, plus practice questions)

Common Pitfalls:
-Students often wonder how the inner core can be solid when the outer core is liquid. They argue that if it is hot enough in the outer core to melt metal, the inner core should also be liquid because it is hotter. The answer is that the temperature required to melt something depends on the pressure – at higher pressures, higher temperatures are needed to melt something. So even though the inner core is hotter than the outer core, the pressure is higher as well – too high to allow for the metal to melt.

Chapter 8 Activity: Solar Nebula Hypothesis

The diagram below shows 5 images representing the formation of the solar system. Place these images in order by matching them with the descriptions below. Also, cirlce the appropriate responses in the descriptions below.

1. _____ The solar system begins as a large, spherical, spinning cloud of gas and dust. About 5 billion years ago, this cloud begins to collapse. Just as an ice skater spins faster as she brings her arms closer to her body, the cloud spins *faster/slower* (circle one) as it collapses.

2. _____ As collapse continues, the cloud flattens out into a disk shape. Gravity causes most of the mass to concentrate *at the edges/in the center* (circle one) of the disk.

3. _____ As collapse proceeds, temperatures in the disk *decrease/increase* (circle one). Eventually temperatures in the center are hot enough that fusion begins and the Sun ignites. In the outer regions of the disk, small regions of matter start to collect.

4. _____ These small regions of collapsing matter grow into moon-sized protoplanets.

5. _____ The protoplanets grow into planets through collisions until most debris and gas has been swept up.

The diagram below show three regions in the early solar system (during the time of planet formation). Region A is where temperatures were above the boiling point of water, region B is where temperatures were below the freezing point of water, and region C is too far away from the center of the disk for there to be large amounts of material.

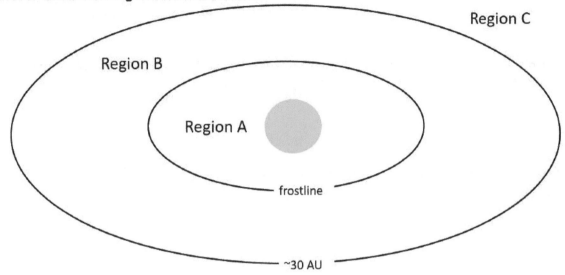

6. In Region A, would the following material have been present as a solid or a gas during planet formation? Complete the chart below.

Material	Solid or Gas?
hydrogen and helium	gas
water	
rocks and metals	solid

7. In Region B, would the following material have been present as a solid or a gas during planet formation? Complete the chart below.

Material	Solid or Gas?
hydrogen and helium	gas
water	
rocks and metals	solid

8. Planets will grow from any available solid material in the region. Given this information, which would grow faster, a planet in Region A or a planet in Region B?

9. In order to hold on to gas and develop an atmosphere, a planet needs to reach a certain size; it must be big enough to have enough gravity to hold that gas in. Based on this and your answer from question 8, which planet will start to sweep up gas first, a planet in Region A or a planet in Region B? Note that by the time the planet in the other region is big enough to sweep up gas, there will not be much gas left.

10. Which planets in our solar system do you think formed in Region A, at temperatures above the boiling point of water?

11. Which planets in our solar system do you think formed in Region B, at temperatures below the freezing point of water?

12. Student A says, *"I think that only Mercury and Venus formed in Region A. That's because those are the only planets where the temperature is too hot for liquid water. Earth couldn't have formed in Region A because the oceans aren't boiling!"*
Student B says, *"I think you are confusing the temperature during formation with the temperature today. It was much hotter during planet formation. So just because the Earth's temperature isn't above boiling right now, doesn't mean that it wasn't above boiling during planet formation. I think the Terrestrial planets formed in Region A and the Jovian planets in Region B. In Region B, there was more solid material because of the ice, so the planets grew faster and were able to sweep up all of the gas before the planets in Region A had a chance!"*

With which student or students do you agree, and why?

13. The plot below shows temperatures in the early solar system. Note that water freezes at 273 K and boils at 373 K (for reference, room temperature is about 296 K). Does this plot agree with your answers from 10 and 11? Why or why not? If not, you may want to go back and rethink some of your answers!

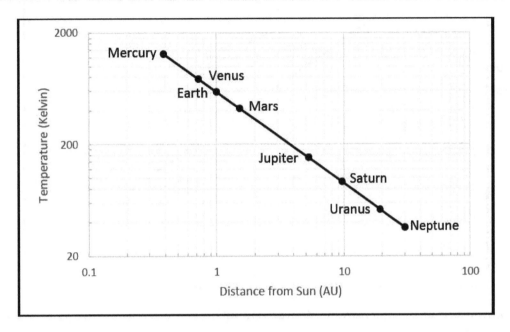

14. Would you expect a Jupiter-like planet to form near the region of Venus? Why or why not?

15. Would you expect a Jupiter-like planet to form beyond Neptune? Why or why not?

16. Imagine a solar system forming around a star that is warmer than our sun. Do you think you would find Jovian planets closer to, the same distance from, or further away from their star than our Jovian planets are to the Sun? Explain your reasoning.

17. The plot below shows the temperature gradient during solar system formation around a star that is hotter than our sun. At what distances would you expect to find Terrestrial planets in this solar system? At what distances would you expect to find Jovian planets?

18. Do your answers to 16 and 17 agree? Why or why not? If not, you may want to go back and rethink some of your answers!

19. Putting it all together: the solar nebula hypothesis was developed to explain certain observations about the solar system. Use what you have learned in this activity to describe how the solar nebula hypothesis explains (or fits in) with each of these observations.

Observation	Explanation
The planets all orbit the Sun in the same direction.	
The planets all orbit the Sun in nearly circular orbits in the same plane.	
Most of the planets spin the same direction.	
There is smaller debris in the solar system (asteroids and Kuiper Belt Objects) that never became part of a planet.	
The small, rocky planets are found closer to the Sun, and the large, gaseous planets are found further away.	

Chapter 9: Shaping Planetary Surfaces

In this chapter, you will learn about the different processes that shape the surfaces of the Terrestrial planets, and will come to an understanding of why the surfaces of the Terrestrial planets are so varied.

Shown in Figure 9.1 is a topographic map of the Earth's surface. Blues are low elevations, reds are high elevations, and greens are medium elevations. If you look at this map carefully, several things should strike out at you. There are higher elevation continents and lower elevation oceans. Ridges, or underwater mountain chains, run through the center of each of the ocean basins. Mountain chains appear to be located primarily along the edges of continents. We would like to be able to explain why these observations are so; e.g. what makes the surface of the Earth look that way it does?

Figure 9.1: Topographic Map of the Earth (http://www.nasa.gov)

In contrast, Figure 9.2 shows a topographic map of Mars' surface. It looks very different from Earth's map. There are no continents, and the planet looks like its been almost divided in half, with higher elevations in the south and lower elevations in the north. There are no ridges through the lower elevations. Mountains do not appear in chains, but appear scattered randomly. Circular depressions, called craters, are common. Thus we would like to explain not just what makes the surface of the Earth look the way it does, but also way makes the surface of Mars, and the other Terrestrial planets, look the way they do. Most importantly, we want to understand why the planets looks so different from eachother!

Figure 9.2: Topographic Map of Mars (http://www.nasa.gov, Mars Global Surveyor)

Five major processes are responsible for shaping the surfaces of most solid surfaces in the solar system. These processes are impact cratering, plate tectonics, volcanism, wind, and water. We will discuss each of these processes in turn.

Figure 9.3: Meteor Crater, Arizona (USGS)

Impact craters are created when rocks from space hit the surface of a planet. The collision creates an explosion, similar to a nuclear bomb detonating, and leaves behind a bowl-shaped scar in the ground. This bowl-shaped scar is called an impact crater.   Figure 9.3 shows an example of an impact crater on the Earth. Note that there are few actual pieces of the rock from space that caused the crater left; the temperature and pressures during an impact event are so high that the rock from space gets vaporized.   The map shown in Figure 9.4 gives you the locations of all known impact craters on the Earth's surface. You might notice that it looks as if there are more craters in North America and Europe, but this is probably an observational bias; there are more scientists in those areas looking for craters. However, it is clear that craters on the Earth are relatively rare.

This is not the case for all Terrestrial bodies. In fact, cratering is THE dominant process on many objects, for example Mercury and the Moon (Figure 9.5). When you look at these surfaces, all you see is crater upon crater upon crater!

Figure 9.4: Locations of Impact Craters on the Earth (NASA Lunar and Planetary Institute)

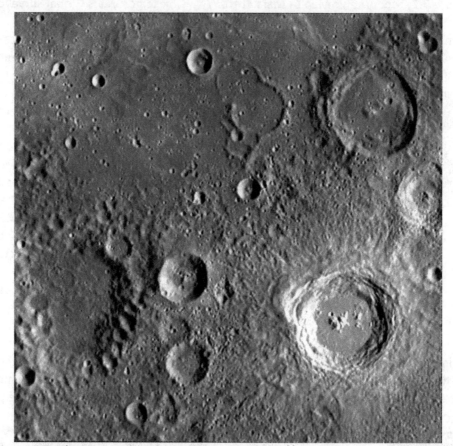

Figure 9.5: The Cratered Surface of Mercury (http://www.nasa.gov, MESSENGER)

The process that is responsible for creating most of the features that we see on the Earth's surface is plate tectonics. The theory of plate tectonics says that the rigid outer surface layer of the Earth is cracked into plates, similar to a hardboiled egg where the shell is all cracked up. This layer is about 100 km thick; analogous to the thickness of an apple's skin relative to the whole apple. The Earth's plates float around on a warm and weak underlying layer at a rate of about a few centimeters per year (this is the same rate that your fingernails grow). As this happens, heat seeps out of the hot, partially molten interior, and plates interact at their boundaries. It is these interactions that create most of the physical features we see at the Earth's surface. The Earth is the only planet that we know of that has plate tectonics. However, recently scientists have discovered that Jupiter's moon Europa may have plate tectonics – with plates made of ice, not rock!

There are three ways that plates can interact at their boundaries, corresponding to three types of plate boundaries. At a divergent plate boundary, plates are moving away from each other. At a convergent plate boundary, plates are moving towards each other. At a transform plate boundary, plates are sliding past one another without colliding or splitting.

Each type of plate boundary is associated with different physical features (illustrated in Figure 9.6). Divergent boundaries typically occur in the middle of the ocean. As the ocean splits apart, magma rises up through the gap, creating a ridge and new seafloor. Thus if you remember back to the topographic map of the Earth, those underwater mountain chains in the middle of the oceans are actually divergent boundaries (called "divergent ridges"). Underwater volcanism and earthquakes are also associated with divergent boundaries. At a convergent boundary, plate collide and generate mountains, volcanoes, deep cracks in the sea floor called trenches, and earthquakes. At transform plate boundaries, earthquakes are generated. This is why there are earthquakes in southern California. There, the North American plate slides past the Pacific plate along the San Andreas fault.

Figure 9.6: Three Types of Plate Boundaries, A is a transform boundary, B is a divergent boundary, and C is a convergent boundary
(https://commons.wikimedia.org/wiki/File:Tectonic_plate_boundaries_clean.png)

Though plate tectonics can generate volcanoes, you don't need plate tectonics to have a volcano. You can also have non-plate tectonic related volcanism at what are termed hot spots. At a hot spot, there is a portion of the interior that is hotter than normal and acts like a flame underneath the surface, creating a volcano. An example of a hot spot on the Earth is Hawaii. An example of hot spot volcanism elsewhere in the solar system is Jupiter's moon Io. In Figure 9.7, we can see not one erupting hot spot volcano on Io, but two!! Hot spot volcanism is an alternative way for a planet to release heat when it doesn't have plate tectonics. Scientists don't yet know why some planets release their heat via plate tectonics and others solely via hot spot volcanism.

Figure 9.7: Erupting Volcanoes on Io
(http://www.nasa.gov, New Horizons)

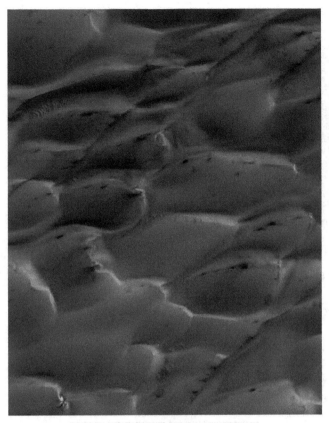

Figure 9.8: Sand Dunes on Mars
(http://www.nasa.gov, Mars Reconnaissance
Orbiter)

Wind can erode and deposit material, forming features like sand dunes (Figure 9.8) and wind streaks (Figure 9.9).

Water can also erode and deposit material. Figure 9.10 shows a stream bed on Mars. Note that it is covered with craters; this indicates that the stream bed is old...water has not flowed through the stream bed for a long time.

We can put what we've learned together and sum up what different features tell us about a planet. Volcanoes indicate that a planet has or had a hot molten interior. Divergent ridges indicate that a planet has or had a hot molten interior and plate tectonics. Sand dunes indicate that a planet has or had an atmosphere. Stream beds indicate that a plate has or had water. Lastly, craters indicate that a feature is old. For example, if we see a volcano with a lot of craters on it, we know that that volcano has not erupted for a long time. Thus there once was a hot interior, but not any longer.

Figure 9.9: Dust Streaks on Mars
(http://www.nasa.gov, Mars Odyssey)

Figure 9.10: Stream Beds on Mars (http://www.nasa.gov; left - Viking Orbiter, right - Mars Express)

Questions You Should Be Able to Answer
1. What five major processes shape planetary surfaces?
2. What does the theory of plate tectonics say?
3. What is a hot spot? How do hot spots differ on a planet with plate tectonics and a planet without plate tectonics?
4. What do volcanoes, divergent ridges, sand dunes, stream beds, and craters tell us about a planet?
5. What do we mean when we say that a planet or moon is "geologically dead?"
6. How is size related to a planet's geologic activity?

Suggestions for Further Reading
1. http://www.lpi.usra.edu/education/explore/shaping_the_planets/background/ (shaping the planets reading)
2. http://iqa.evergreenps.org/science/phy_science/tutorials/astrotutorials/Shaping/GeoProcess.html (shaping planetary surfaces tutorial, with practice questions)

Common Pitfalls
-Just because a planet has volcanoes does not necessarily mean it has plate tectonics. Plate tectonics *can* form volcanoes, but hot spots (which are non-plate tectonic related) can also form volcanoes.

Chapter 9 Activity: Planet Surface Features

Part 1: Surface Processes

1. Circle the feature that a planet must have if it has recently formed volcanoes. If none of the features are required, write "none."

      atmosphere   hot interior   liquid water   plate tectonics

2. Circle the feature that a planet must have if it has recently formed sand dunes. If none of the features are required, write "none."

      atmosphere   hot interior   liquid water   plate tectonics

3. Circle the feature that a planet must have if it has recently formed craters. If none of the features are required, write "none."

      atmosphere   hot interior   liquid water   plate tectonics

4. Circle the feature that a planet must have if it has recently formed divergent ridges. If none of the features are required, write "none." [Hint: Two features must be circled here.]

      atmosphere   hot interior   liquid water   plate tectonics

5. Circle the feature that a planet must have if it has recently formed stream beds. If none of the features are required, write "none."

      atmosphere   hot interior   liquid water   plate tectonics

Part 2: Terrestrial Bodies

The diagrams below show pictures taken for the Terrestrial planets and the moon. Label the features in each picture with the terms: stream bed, volcanoes, crater, sand dune, or divergent ridge. Images are all NASA images (http://www.nasa.gov) unless otherwise stated.

MERCURY

Feature:_____
(answer is not Mickey Mouse!)

Feature:_____

VENUS

Feature:_____

Feature: <u>wind streak</u>
(same process as sand dunes)

Feature:_____
(https://commons.wikimedia.org/wiki/File:Fuego_Eruption,_March_30,_.2013.jpg)

Feature:_____

Feature:_____

Feature:_____

E
A
R
T
H

MOON

Feature:_____

Feature:_____

MARS

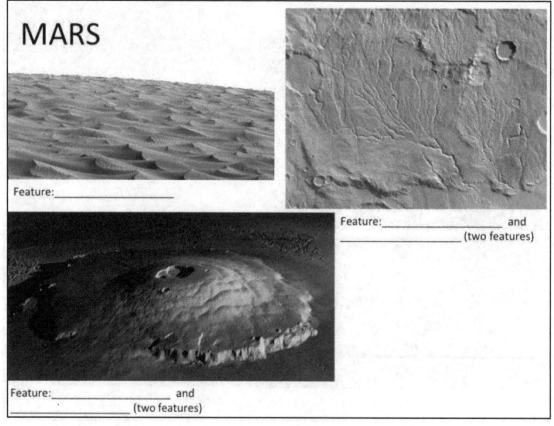

Feature:_____

Feature:_____ and
_____ (two features)

Feature:_____ and
_____ (two features)

Using what you learned from the images above, fill out the table below. Choose from the options: yes, no, or in past.

	Hot Interior?	Plate Tectonics?	Liquid Water?	Atmosphere?
Mercury				
Venus				
Earth				
Moon				
Mars				

Chapter 9 Activity: Planetary Evolution

Part 1: Geologically Dead Planets versus Geologically Active Planets

A planet or moon is considered geologically dead when it:

> (1) no longer has a hot, partially molten interior to fuel plate tectonics or volcanism, and
> (2) no longer has an atmosphere.

On a geologically dead body the only significant modification of the surface is from impact cratering.

1. Below is a list of planets and moons. Circle the two which can be considered geologically dead. Explain your choice.

     Mercury   Venus   Earth   the Moon

2. Below is a list of planets and moons. Circle the two which can be considered geologically active. Explain your choice.

     Mercury   Venus   Earth   the Moon

3. It is hard to put Mars into a category because it has characteristics of both a geologically dead planet and a geologically active planet.

How is Mars like a geologically dead planet?

How is it like a geologically active planet?

4. A student says, "planets that are closer to the Sun receive more heat and thus remain geologically active for a longer time than planets that are further from the Sun." What evidence can you cite to this student to prove that he/she is wrong?

Part 2: Rate of Cooling

4. Imagine a cup of boiling water and a pot of boiling water. Which will cool more quickly?

5. After formation, the planets were all at roughly the same temperature. Imagine a small planet and a big planet. Which will cool more quickly?

6. A planet no longer releases heat due to plate tectonics or volcanism when it has cooled to the point where none or little of the interior remains molten. Which planet will reach that point more quickly – a small planet or a big planet?

7. All planets slowly lose their atmospheres, but bigger planets hold on to gases much more easily and thus lose their atmosphere more slowly. Which planet will lose its atmosphere first – a small planet or a big planet?

8. Which planet will become geologically dead first – a small planet or a big planet? Explain your answer.

9. The below image shows the relative sizes of Mercury, Venus, Earth, the Moon, and Mars. Why are Mercury and the Moon geologically dead, but not Venus and the Earth? Why does Mars have characteristics of both a dead planet and an active planet?

10. Do you think that the Earth will always be geologically active? Why or why not?

Part 3: Putting It All Together

11. You discover a new solar system. The solar system has five terrestrial planets, whose masses and distances from the Sun are shown in the table below. List the planets in order from the planet that will become geologically dead first to the planet that will become geologically dead last. Explain your reasoning.

	Mass (In terms of Earth's mass)	Distance from Sun (in AU)
Planet A	3 times	0.2 AU
Planet B	2 times	0.4 AU
Planet C	0.5 times	1 AU
Planet D	5 times	1.5 AU
Planet E	0.1 times	2.1 AU

12. Student A says, "*I think that planets closer to the Sun will remain hotter longer because they receive more energy from the Sun. So I put E-D-C-B-A.*"

Student B says, "*But its not the heat from the Sun that matters, it is the planets' internal heat. All the planets start off the same temperature and cool. Smaller planets will lose their heat and their atmospheres faster. So I put E-C-B-A-D.*"

With which student(s) do you agree, and why?

13. The presence of which features depend *only* on the planet's size, and not on its distance from the Sun? (Circle all that apply...hint: there are three).

      volcanoes   sand dunes   divergent ridges   craters   stream beds

14. Which feature depends on the planet's size, but *also* depends on the planet's surface temperature, which is directly related to the planet's distance to the Sun? (Circle one).

      volcanoes   sand dunes   divergent ridges   craters   stream beds

15. Which feature will form no matter what, regardless of size of distance? (Circle one).

    volcanoes   sand dunes   divergent ridges   craters   stream beds

16. Suppose that there was a Mercury-sized planet between the orbits of Mars and Jupiter. Circle the features that you expect to be actively forming on this planet. Explain your reasoning.

volcanoes   stream beds
divergent ridges   craters
sand dunes

17. Suppose that there was an Earth-sized planet between the orbits of Mars and Jupiter. Circle the features that you expect to be actively forming on this planet. Explain your reasoning.

volcanoes   stream beds
divergent ridges   craters
sand dunes

18. Student A says, *"Because the planet is the same size as the Earth, it should have all the same features as the Earth. So I circled everything."*

Student B says, *"Except the planet is further from the Sun, so it will be colder. It can't have any of these features because it'll be too cold! So I just circled craters."*

Student C says, *"You're right that the surface will be colder, so there won't be any stream beds because any water be frozen. But since the planet is big like the Earth, it will still be hot inside and it will still have an atmosphere. So I circled everything but stream beds."*

With which student(s) do you agree, and why?

Chapter 10: Planetary Compositions

In this chapter, you will learn what planets are composed of. We will talk about what makes up the surfaces of the planets (rocks), and then we will talk about how scientists study the interiors of planets.

There are three types of rocks that can be found on the surface of a planet: igneous, sedimentary and metamorphic. Each rock type forms in a different way, and so tells us something different about the forces active on a planet (Figure 10.1).

	Source Material	Rock-Forming Process	Examples
Igneous	melting of rocks	crystallization (cooling and solidification of melted rock)	basalt, granite
Sedimentary	weathering and erosion of rocks into small bits (sediment)	deposition, burial, and lithification (cementing pieces together) of sediment	shale, sandstone
Metamorphic	rocks subjected to high pressures and temperatures	Recrystallization in solid state (rearrangement of atoms without melting)	gneiss, slate

Figure 10.1: Different Rock Types Form in Different Ways

Igneous rocks form when molten, liquid rock (lava or magma) cools and solidifies. To get lava you need a volcano, and to get a volcano you need a hot, partially molten interior. Thus the presence of igneous rocks on a planet implies a hot molten interior when the rocks formed. All of the terrestrial planets started out with hot, partially molten interiors initially, so igneous rocks can be found on all of them.

Sedimentary rocks form when rocks are broken apart into pieces and then essentially glued back together again (this is known as lithification). The "glue" comes from minerals precipitated by water. Thus the presence of sedimentary rocks on a planet implies liquid water on the surface when the rocks formed. Sedimentary rocks can be found on the Earth and Mars, implying that though the Martian surface is currently cold and dry, liquid water once ran across it.

Metamorphic rocks form when rocks are subjected to high temperatures and pressures. For this to happen on a significant scale and be exposed on a planet's surface, you need plate tectonics. Thus the presence of metamorphic rocks on a planet implies plate tectonics on the surface when the rocks formed. The only planet to have or had plate tectonics that we know of is the Earth, so metamorphic rocks are expected only on the Earth's surface.

Now what if we want to study the interior of a planet? How can we do this? One option you might suggest is drilling; if we want to know what the inside of the Earth looks like, why don't we just drill a deep hole? The Russians had a project from 1970-1989 to do just this. However, in 19 years of drilling, they only got down 12 km (or 7.5 miles). This might seem deep...until you remember that the Earth is about 6,700 km to the center! Thus, 12 km is only 0.18% of the way to the center. In other words, if the Earth were an apple, we haven't even drilled past the skin.

Figure 10.2: Xenoliths (the light chunks) (https://commons.wikimedia.org/wiki/File:Peridotite_xen oliths2.tif

Another suggestion that you might come up with is to look at rocks spewed up by volcanoes from the Earth's interior. Such rocks are called xenoliths (Figure 10.2), which literally means "strange rock" in Latin. However, it turns out that the deepest xenoliths come from depths of about 300 km. This is better than before: xenoliths can tell us what the layer just under the surface looks like, but it's still not great. 300 km is still only 4.5% of the way to the center. Thus if we want to know what the center of the Earth is like, we are going to need to be more creative.

One option is to look at meteorites. Meteorites are extraterrestrial material that falls to Earth. Most meteorites are from the asteroid belt; they are the leftover material from which the Earth formed. Thus by looking at meteorites, we can get a general idea of what elements make up the Earth. It's like looking at a messy kitchen after someone makes a cake to take a guess at what's in the cake (flour on the floor, egg shells in the sink, so on...). What we learn when we look at meteorites is that there is a lot more metal (notably iron) in them than we see at the Earth's surface. This suggests that somewhere in the Earth, there is significant amounts of metal.

The fact that the Earth has a magnetic field further suggests that this metal is liquid. This is because we know from physics that to create a magnetic field, you need liquid, moving metal.

We can use the overall average density of the Earth to estimate the amount of metal. The density of an object is its mass divided by its volume. You can think of the density of an object as how compact the atoms that make up the object are. If the atoms are more compact, the object is denser. Keep in mind that density is not the same thing as weight. A large hunk of iron and a small hunk of iron will have the same density because the atoms making up the hunks are equally compact, but the large hunk will weigh more because there is more of it. Thus density does not depend on the size of something, but only on what something is made of. In general, ice and gas have a density of about 1000 kg/m^3, rock has a density of about 3000 kg/m^3, and metal has a density of about 8000 kg/m^3. So if a planet were made entirely of metal, it would have a density of 8000 kg/m^3. If a planet were made entirely of rock, it would have a density of 3000 kg/m^3. If a planet were made of exactly half metal and half rock, it would have a density of 5500 kg/m^3 (exactly in between 3000 and 8000). The average density of the Earth is 4070 kg/m^3, in between these two numbers. This indicates that the Earth is made of both rock and metal, with more rock than metal. As another example, Jupiter has an average density of 1300 kg/m³. This indicates that Jupiter is made mostly of ice and gas with a little bit of rock.

So far, we have talked about several methods which give us some information about planets' interiors. However, we have not yet talked about the most significant one for the Earth. Most of our information about the Earth's interior comes from studying seismic waves, or earthquake waves.

Earthquakes are a sudden release of energy and the subsequent shaking of the ground. Any event that releases a large amount of energy all at once can cause an earthquake - things like faulting, volcanic eruptions, bomb blasts, meteorite impacts, and landslides. Most of the Earth's earthquakes are created by faulting due to plate tectonics.

Once an earthquake occurs, its energy is radiated away from the origin of the earthquake in the form of seismic waves, which are waves that shake the ground that they travel though. This is analogous to dropping a pebble in a pond and watching the waves ripple outward in all directions from the drop.

Seismic waves can be measured using seismometers, which are instruments that record the motion of the ground over time. The ground motion is recorded in a series of squiggles known as a seismogram.

A typical seismogram will show three distinct sets of waves (Figure 10.3). The first set is known as the P-wave (or Primary wave), the second set is known as the S-wave (or Secondary wave) and the final set is known as the Surface waves. P and S waves are both types of body waves, meaning they travel through the Earth's interior. In contrast, surface waves can only travel through layers near the Earth's surface. Since we are interested in the Earth's interior, we are going to focus on the body waves.

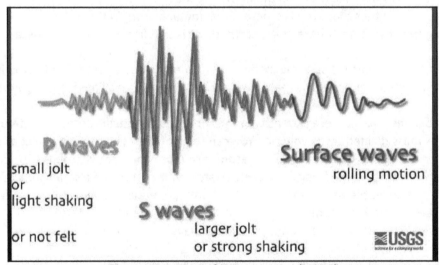

Figure 10.3: Typical Seismogram (USGS)

The two types of body waves differ in several important ways. P-waves push and pull the rock that they travel through, S-waves shear it side-to-side or up-and-down (Figure 10.4). P waves travel

116

faster than S-waves. Lastly, P-waves can travel through solid and liquid, but S-waves can only travel through solids.

By observing the speeds and patterns of body waves as they travel through the Earth, scientists can learn about the Earth's interior. For example, let's suppose an earthquake occurs at the star in Figure 10.5. The paths of S-waves from this earthquake are shown by the arrows. Note that Seismic stations within 103 degrees of the source will observe both P and S waves from this earthquake. However, notice that when S-waves try to go through the core, they get blocked. This means that seismic stations on the opposite side of the Earth will observe only P-waves. No S-waves will be recorded; this is known as the S-wave shadow zone (gray hashed region in Figure 10.5). Recall that

Figure 10.4: P and S Waves
(https://commons.wikimedia.org/w/index.php?title=Sp ecial:Search&limit=50&offset=20&profile=default&sear ch=seismic+waves#/media/File:Pswaves_ro.jpg)

S-waves can't travel through liquid. Thus, the S-wave shadow zone tells scientists that the core of the Earth must be liquid. The liquid core blocks S-waves from reaching the shadow zone. The size of the core can be constrained by the size of the shadow zone. The bigger the shadow zone, the bigger the core must be.

We can sum up the structure of the Earth into three compositional layers (Figure 10.6). The outer layer, the crust, ranges from 0-60 km thick and is composed of low density rocks. The crust is very thin relative to the Earth as whole; a good comparison is the skin of an apple relative to the whole apple. The middle layer, the mantle, is composed of high density rocks and goes from below the crust to 2900 km deep. At the center is the core, which is made of metal, primarily iron (95% iron and 5% nickel). There are two parts to the core; the outer core and the inner core. The outer core is liquid, and the inner core is solid. This might seem counterintuitive to you; if the Earth is hot enough to melt iron at the outer core, why not the inner core as well? The answer is that melting

Figure 10.5: S Wave Shadow Zone

temperature depends on pressure. Though the inner core is hotter than the outer core, the pressure is higher, making it solid.

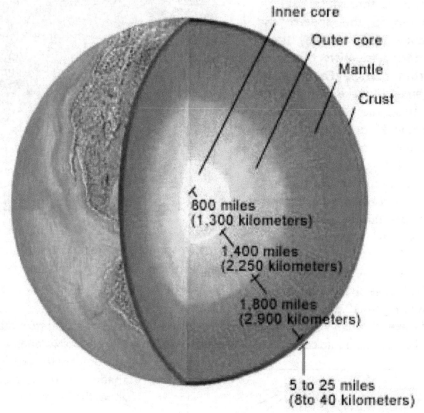

Figure 8.2: Layers of the Earth
(https://commons.wikimedia.org/wiki/File:Earth_layers_NASA.png)

Questions You Should Be Able to Answer
1. What are the three different types of rocks? How does each type form? What does each type tell us about the planet it is found on?
2. How do scientists determine the interior structure of the Earth?
3. What is density? How can density be used to determine what the inside of a planet is like?
4. What is an earthquake?
5. What causes earthquakes?
6. What is a seismic wave?
7. What are the two types of seismic waves? What is the difference between them?
8. What are the two types of body waves? What is the difference between them?
9. How do scientists use seismic waves to determine the interior structure of the Earth?
10. How do we know that the Earth's outer core is liquid?
11. Describe the following layers of the Earth: crust, mantle, outer core, inner core.

Suggestions for Further Reading
1. http://ratw.asu.edu/aboutrocks.html (about rocks)

2. http://www.khanacademy.org/science/cosmology-and-astronomy/earth-history-topic/seismic-waves-tutorial/v/seismic-waves (Khan Academy explains seismic waves)

Common Pitfalls

-Remember that the density of an object depends only on its material make-up, NOT its size! For example, a 10 pound rock has a lower density than a penny because the atoms that make up metal are more compact than the atoms that make up rock. The fact that that rock weighs more does not affect the density, it just means there is a lot of it!

Chapter 10 Activity: Density

Part 1: What is density?

Density is the amount of material in a given volume. Mathematically, it is mass divided by volume, where mass is the amount of matter in an object and volume is the amount of space an object takes up. Thus density can be thought of as how compact something is. *If two objects are the same size*, but one is heavier, it is more dense. *If two objects are NOT the same size*, then the heavier one is not necessarily more dense!

1. For each of the four rows below, circle which object has a higher density:

a bucket of ping pong balls	or	a bucket of golf balls	or	they have the same density
	or		or	they have the same density
a small rock	or	a large rock	or	they have the same density
	or		or	they have the same density

2. **Student 1** says, "I think a small rock is less dense than a large one. When you pick them up, the small rock is much lighter than the big rock. Since density is the same thing as weight, a heavier rock is a denser rock."

   Student 2 says, "I think things with the same density but different sizes can have different weights. The atoms in the two rocks are equally compact, so the density is the same."

   Student 3 says, "I think it is easiest to compare things the same size. If you broke a piece off the big rock that was the same size as the little rock, they would have the same weight, so that means that rocks have the same density."

   With which student or students do you agree with and why?

Part 2: Density as a clue to a planet's interior.

Different materials have different densities. For example, rock has a density of about 3000 kg/m3, metals have a density of about 8000 kg/m3, and ices and gases have densities of about 1000 kg/m3 or less.

The bulk, or average, density of a planet can tell us something about what the planet is made of.

3. The surface of the Earth is composed of rock, and thus has a density of 3000 kg/m3. However, the bulk density of the Earth is 4070 kg/m3. Given this information, what do you think the center of the Earth (the core) is composed of? Explain your reasoning.

4. The picture below shows 6 planets. In these pictures, light gray represents ices and gases, medium gray represents rock, and black represents metal. For each planet, give an estimate of the density. The first one is done for you.

    A: somewhere between 1000 kg/m3 and 3000 kg/m3, ~2000 kg/m3

    B: _____

    C: _____

    D: _____

    E: _____

    F: _____

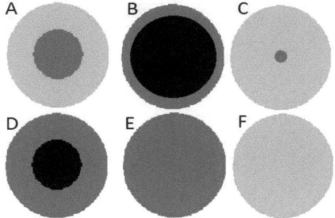

5. Rank the planets' densities from question four from greatest to least.

_____ > _____ > _____ > _____ > _____ > _____

6. The planets in the previous two questions were all the same size. Would your answers change if some of the planets were bigger and some were smaller, but the material makeup of each planet did not change? Explain your answer.

7. **Student 1** says, "I think the answers would change if the planets were different sizes. That's because bigger planets will be heavier and thus will be denser. In this case, I would rank the planets by size."

Student 2 says, "Just because a planet is bigger and heavier doesn't mean it is denser. Remember we learned that the Jovian planets are bigger than the Terrestrial planets, but they are still less dense because they are made of gas, not rock. With density all that matters is what something is made of. Size doesn't matter, because density is just how compact something is. That's distinct from mass and weight, which both depend on much stuff there is in a planet." So I think the answers wouldn't change.

With which student or students do you agree with and why?

Chapter 10 Activity: Earth's Interior

Part A – PREM

The diagram below is the "Preliminary Reference Earth Model." It shows the density of the Earth with depth. 0 represents the middle of the earth; the surface is 6,356 km. The image is from http://www.gps.caltech.edu/uploads/File/People/dla/DLApepi81.pdf (accessed on Wikimedia Commons). A boundary called the "Moho Discontinuity is marked." Question 1-7 refer to this plot.

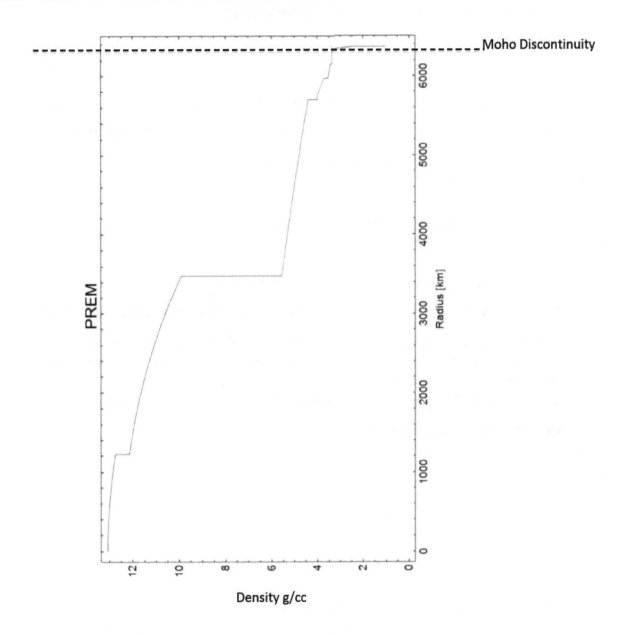

1. Generally, does the density increase or decrease with depth? Why?

2. The Moho Discontinuity is a boundary that marks a distinct change in the rate at which density changes with depth. How does the rate of change vary both above and below the discontinuity?

Above: Density changes   *quickly / slowly*   (circle one) with depth.

Below: Density changes   *quickly / slowly*   (circle one) with depth.

3. The layer above the Moho Discontinuity is called the crust. Label the crust on the diagram.

4. Which of the following is most similar to the thickness of the crust relative to the whole Earth?

      a. The thickness of an apple skin relative to the whole apple.

      b. The thickness of an orange peel relative to the whole orange.

      b. The thickness of a peach relative to the peach pit.

5. Two students are discussing their answers to question 4:

Student 1 says, "I put the orange, because the Earth's crust is the thinnest layer, but it's not that thin."

Student 2 says, "But the Earth's crust is only about 35 km thick on average. This means that the crust makes up only about 0.55% of the Earth's radius! Oranges are about 1.5 inches in diameter, with peels about ¼ inch thick. This means that the orange peel makes up a much greater percent of the oranges radius – like 17%. So I think we need something that is thinner – this is why I chose the apple."

With which student do you agree and why?

6. There are two other distinct boundaries on the density plot, where the density suddenly increases (NOT the small one at about 5600 km!). Draw dashed lines to demarcate these boundaries.

7. The layer below the crust is the mantle, the layer below that is the outer core, and the layer at the center is the inner core. Label these layers on the density plot.

Part 2 – Size of the Core

The diagram below shows the Earth. The location of an earthquake is shown by the star. Stations that record both P and S waves from this earthquake are marked by black dots, and stations that record only P waves are marked by gray dots. Questions 1-4 refer to this diagram.

1. For each station that recorded an S-wave, draw lines representing the travel path of the wave from the earthquake to the station.

2. Why is there a zone where no S-waves are recorded?

3. Sketch in the boundary of the core on your diagram.

4. Label the crust, mantle, and core in your diagram.

5. What is the state of the mantle? Circle one.

      mostly liquid   mostly solid

6. What is the state of the outer core? Circle one.

      mostly liquid   mostly solid

7. Three students are discussing where the lava that is erupted by Earth's volcanoes from:

Student 1 says, "Since the mantle is solid and the outer core is liquid, I think that the lava must come from the outer core."

Student 2 says, "But the outer core is metal, and volcanoes aren't erupting liquid metal. So I think that the mantle must be liquid too and that's were the lava comes from."

Student 3 says, "I think you're both a little confused. It's true that the outer core is liquid, but the lava can't come from there because lava is not made of metal – it's rock. And it's true that the mantle is solid – but its only *mostly* solid. There must be small pockets of liquid here and there that the lava comes from."

Which student(s) do you agree with and why?

8. How would you be able to tell if a planet's outer core had solidified?

Chapter 11: Crater Dating

In this chapter, you will learn how scientists use craters to determine the ages of planetary surfaces.

Figure 11.1: Typical Crater on the Moon
(http://www.nasa.gov, Apollo 17)

An impact crater forms when solar system debris (typically from the asteroid belt, but sometimes a comet) hits the surface of a planet or moon. The collision creates an explosion and leaves behind a bowl-shaped depression, or crater. Around the crater there will be debris that was thrown out during the impact; this is known as the ejecta blanket. A typical impact crater on the moon is shown in Figure 11.1; the ejecta blanket is the lighter colored material surrounding the crater.

The size of the crater that forms depends on the gravity of the planet or moon that is hit, the size of the impactor, and the speed that the impactor is traveling. However, to give you some idea, here are crater sizes for typical different sized impactors on the Earth. A 10 ft in diameter meteor will create a crater that is 620 feet across - this is 2 football fields! A 100 ft meteor gives you a crater that is 3/4 of a mile across, a 1,000 ft meteor gives you a crater that is 5 miles across, and a 10 mile meteor gives you a crater that is 200 miles across (the later is the size of the meteor that caused the extinction of the dinosaurs 65 million years ago).

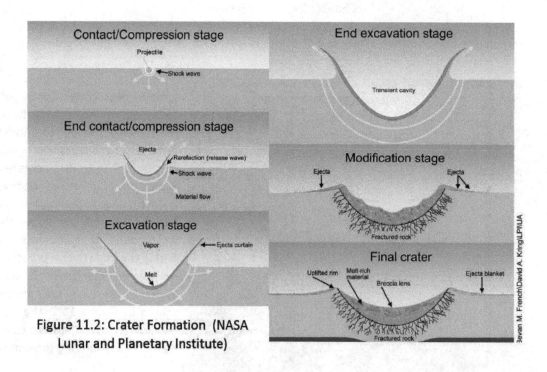

Figure 11.2: Crater Formation (NASA Lunar and Planetary Institute)

Figure 11.2 illustrates crater formation. A meteor comes in, and embeds itself into the surface. The energy from the impact sets up an explosion very similar to a nuclear bomb being detonated. The explosion throws material upward and outward, creating the crater and the ejecta blanket. Most of the meteor itself is vaporized due to the extremely high pressures and temperatures.

Craters can give scientists a sequence of events by looking at overlapping (cross-cutting) relationships. If two craters overlap, then the crater on the top is younger than the crater on the bottom (Figure 11.3a). In other words, the crater on the bottom happened first and the crater on top happened second. Visible ejecta rays form at the same time as the crater, and so are included in the rule. For example, in Figure 11.3b, the crater with rays is younger than the crater without rays. As another example, in Figure 11.3c, the crater with rays is older than the crater without rays. If two craters don't overlap then we can't say which is older (Figure 11.3d).

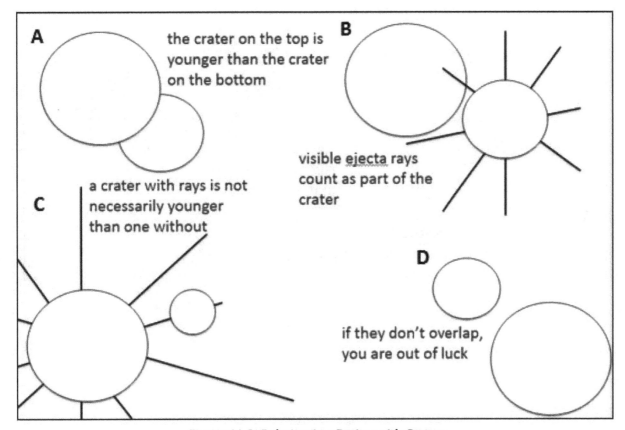

A   the crater on the top is younger than the crater on the bottom

B   visible ejecta rays count as part of the crater

C   a crater with rays is not necessarily younger than one without

D   if they don't overlap, you are out of luck

Figure 11.3: Relative Age Dating with Craters

Sometimes craters have been filled in with lava (which typically cools to the igneous rock basalt). If this is the case, the craters that are filled in with lava came before the lava, and the craters that are not filled in with lava came after the lava. In Figure 11.4a, the bottom crater formed, then the crater was filled in with lava, and then the top crater formed. In Figure 11.4b, both craters are infilled with lava, so the lava must have come last. Thus, first the unrayed crater formed, then the rayed crater, and then both were filled with lava. Note that if two craters don't overlap, but one is filled with lava, we can now get a sequence of events (Figure 11.4d). The crater that is filled with lava must be older because it has to come before the lava and the crater that is not filled with lava must be younger because it has to come after the lava.

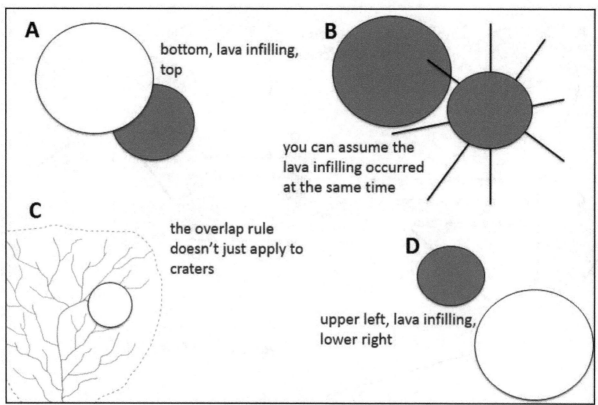

Figure 11.4: Relative Age Dating with Craters, continued

Not only do craters give us a sequence of events, but the number of craters tells us something about a surface's age. The age of a surface refers to the last time that it was significantly changed. This can be via volcanism, wind and/or water activity, or plate tectonics. Basically anything that erases the surface and forms or exposes new rock counts. If a scientist tells you than a certain area of Mars is 100 million years old, she means that it's been 100 million years since anything significant like this happened.

To see how this works, let's imagine two areas on the same planet. Since they are on the same planet, they experience the same cratering rate: all areas on a planet's surface are equally likely to hit by craters. On average, each time a crater forms on one surface, a crater forms on the other surface. Thus over time the surfaces accumulate the same number of craters. As time goes on, more and more craters are added.

But then something happens that erases all of the craters on one of the surfaces...maybe volcanism, maybe plate tectonics, it doesn't matter what. Now this surface has a clean slate. As time continues to go on, both surfaces will continue to accumulate craters at the same rate, but the surface that was erased will always have less craters because it was modified more recently.

We can generalize this into the observation that the number of craters gives a surface's relative age. The more craters a surface has, the older it is. The fewer craters a surface has, the younger it is. In other words, the surface with fewer craters was modified more recently.

If you know the cratering rate, then you can get the actual numerical age. For example, suppose the cratering rate is 1 crater every 1 million years. This means that a surface with 9 craters is 9 million years old and a surface with 3 craters is 3 million years old.

The difficulty with this is that rock samples are needed to constrain the cratering rate (through radiometric dating). However, once the cratering rate is known, you can go back and determine the age anywhere on the planet. For example, let's suppose you send an astronaut to a region of the moon with 9 craters and he brings back rock samples. You use radiometric dating to determine the age of the rocks at 3 million years. This tells you that the cratering rate is 3 craters every 1 million years (9 craters divided by 3 million years). You can then use that rate to determine the age any other surface on the moon. For example, a surface with 3 craters must be 1 million years old since 3 craters form every 1 million years.

Unfortunately, the only solar system body for which we have samples of known origin is the Earth's moon. So the cratering rate is only definitively known for the Moon. However, scientists estimate the cratering rate for other bodies (like Mars or Venus) by taking the Moon's cratering rate and adjusting for size (bigger bodies have more gravity and so pull in more objects) and location in the solar system (the closer you are to the asteroid belt, the more cratering there will be). Lastly, it should be noted that the cratering rate is not constant; it changes with time. Scientists need to account for this as well when determining surface ages.

Questions You Should Be Able to Answer
1. What is an impact crater? How are impact craters formed?
2. Be able to do relative age dating using impact craters, such as done in class and on the homework.
3. How can I tell the relative age of a surface using craters?
4. What do I need to determine the absolute (numerical age) of a surface using craters?

Suggestions for Practice
1. http://astro.unl.edu/classaction/questions/terrplanets/ca_terrplanets_cratersandage1.html (surface ages questions)
2. http://astro.unl.edu/classaction/questions/terrplanets/ca_terrplanets_cratersandage2.html (more surface ages questions)

Chapter 11 Activity: Craters – The Order of Events

1. In the diagram below, there are four pairs of craters. For each pair, number the craters from oldest (formed first) to youngest (formed last). If any of the craters are filled with lava, also give the lava a number (so in these cases, there will be three numbers).

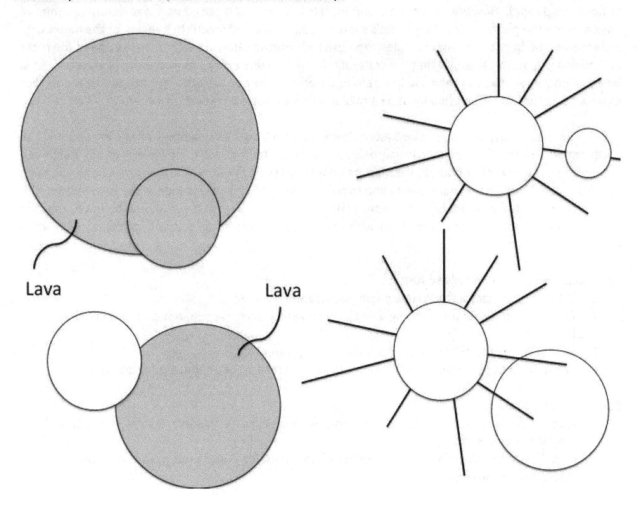

Lava

Lava

2. In the image below, put the events in order from oldest (formed first) to youngest (formed last). If you cannot determine the relative age between two events, use an equals sign.

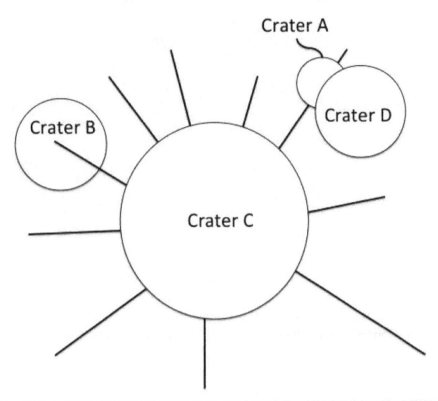

3. In the image below, put the events in order from oldest (formed first) to youngest (formed last). If you cannot determine the relative age between two events, use an equals sign.

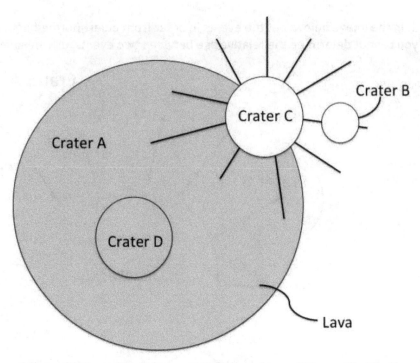

4. In the image below, put the events in order from oldest (formed first) to youngest (formed last). If you cannot determine the relative age between two events, use an equals sign.

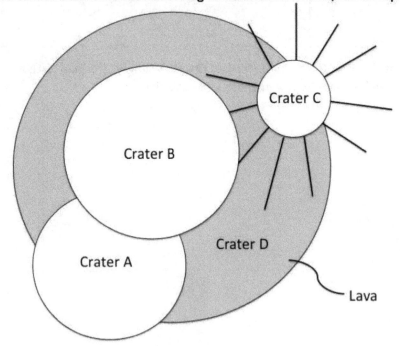

Chapter 11 Activity: Crater Dating

Part 1: Money Analogy

Susan and Tom both work at the same job, making the same hourly wage. They both save all of their money.

1. Susan has $200 and Tom has $150. Who worked more hours?

2. Can you say how many more hours Susan worked than Tom? Why or why not?

3. If the hourly wage is $10 per/hour, now can you say how many more hours Susan worked than Tom? If so, how many?

4. If the hourly wage is $5/hour, how many more hours did Susan work than Tom?

5. Ann works at the same job, making $5 per hour. She has $250 in her bank account. How many hours did Ann work?

6. Match the statements on the right from the money analogy to the statements on the left for relative crater dating. Please note the "age" of a surface refers to how long it has been since the area was resurfaced (craters were erased from water, lava, etc.). If we say a surface is 30 million years old, we mean that it was last resurfaced 30 million years ago, and has been accumulating craters since then.

Susan, Ann, and Tom make the same hourly wage.	Once a crater forms on a surface, it doesn't disappear unless resurfacing occurs.
We assume Susan, Ann, and Tom save their money.	The area with the most craters is the oldest.
The more hours you work, the more money you have.	All areas on a planet's surface experience the same cratering rate.
The person with the most money has worked the most hours.	If you know the cratering rate, you can determine the exact age of a surface.
If you know the hourly wage, you can determine exactly how many hours Susan, Ann, and Tom worked.	The older an area is, the more craters it has.

Part 2: Crater Dating

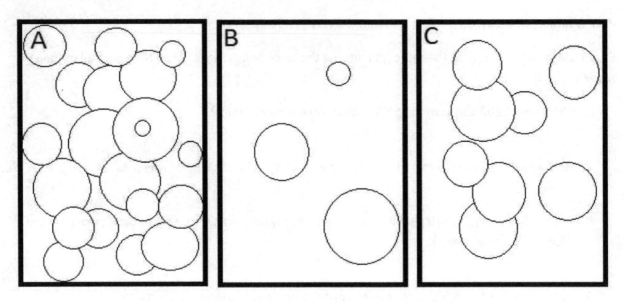

7. Rank the ages of the three surfaces shown above from oldest to youngest: ___ > ___ > ___

8. Based on just the images, can you tell what the numerical age difference is between B and C? Why or why not?

9. You send a spaceship to collect samples from area C and determine the area is 4 million years old. What is the cratering rate? (Note cratering rate = number of craters / time).

10. Using the cratering rate you determine from 9, how old are areas A and B? (Note time = number of craters / cratering rate).

11. In the image below, do you think that all parts of the surface shown are the same age? Why or why not?

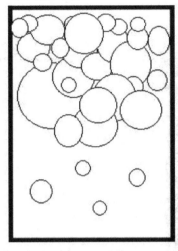

12. **Student 1** says, "There are craters in all parts of the image, so I think that the entire image is the same age."
Student 2 says, "But the bottom has less craters than the top. So I think the bottom must be older."
Student 3 says, "The bottom does have less craters, but that means it's younger. Since the bottom has less craters, that means it was resurfaced more recently and hasn't had as much time to accumulate craters. So the top is older, since it's been longer since resurfacing."
With which student or students do you agree with and why?

Part 3: Cratering Rates Can Change

The image below shows three cratered surfaces on the same planet. The age of each surface is given.

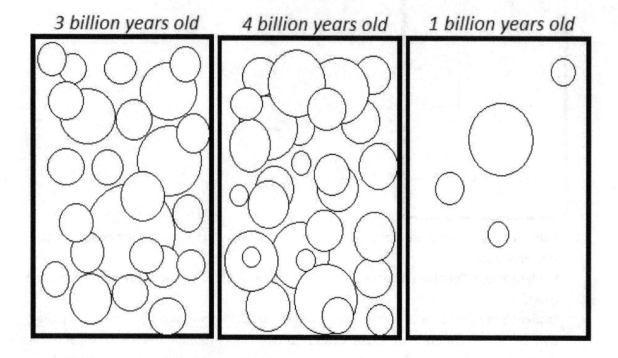

3 *billion years old*   4 *billion years old*   1 *billion years old*

13. How many craters formed in the past 1 billion years?

14. What was the cratering rate for the past 1 billion years?

15. Suppose that the cratering rate was the same from 3 billion years ago to present. If this were the case, how many craters would the area on the left have?

16. How many craters does the area on the left have?

17. From 3 billion to 1 billion years ago, was the cratering rate higher or lower than it was from 1 billion years ago to present?

18. If the area on the left were 1 billion years old, it would have the same number of craters as the area on the right. This means that the rest of the craters must have formed from 3 billion to 1 billion years ago. How many craters is this?

19. What was the cratering rate from 3 billion to 1 billion years ago?

20. Using the same logic and the image in the middle, what was the cratering rate from 4 billion to 3 billion years ago?

21. On the plot below, sketch how the cratering rate has changed over time for this planet.

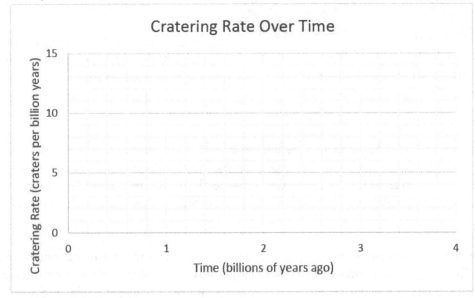

Chapter 12: Impact Hazards

In this chapter, you will learn about the hazards that impact events pose. We will discuss the effects of large and small impact events, the frequency with which such events occur, and possible mitigation strategies.

Figure 12.1: Scars Left by the Impact of Comet-Shoemaker Levy on Jupiter (http://www.nasa.gov, Hubble)

This is a topic that has often has been featured in films, for example Armageddon and Deep Impact. Today we will see just how realistic these films are! It is worth first noting that large impacts *do still happen*. For example, in July of 1994, the 3-mile in diameter comet Shoemaker-Levy impacted into Jupiter, breaking up into pieces at it did so. The explosions left behind dark scars in the atmosphere and released more energy than the world's total nuclear arsenal combined (Figure 12.1). The dark scars took several months to dissipate. A similar sized impact on the Earth would cause global devastation and the likely extinction of the human species.

How do scientists know what happens when a meteor hits the surface? Two ways: by going out into the field and looking at the craters left behind by impacts on the Earth and by using computer simulations.

Let's look first at the effects of a very large impact, such as the impact that formed Chicxulub crater. Chicxulub crater is a 200 mile wide crater on the Yucatan Pensinsula in Mexico. It was created when a 10 mile wide asteroid (this is about twice the height of Mount Everest for reference...!) hit the surface 65 million years ago. Scientists believe that the dinosaurs went extinct because of this impact event.

The Earth experienced several negative effects both on the short term and long term scale after this impact. The energy of the impact immediately triggered earthquakes and tsunamis (tidal waves), and a heated vapor plume (essentially a fireball of thermal radiation). The vapor plume and hot ejecta falling back to the Earth led to massive, global forest fires. In the months to years following the impact, the dust and soot thrown out by the impact and subsequent fires blocked photosynthesis, leading to an impact winter and a collapse of the food chain. It is estimated that the dust and soot would have made it too dark to see for 1 to 6 months, and that photosynthesis would have been blocked for 2 months to a year. The dust and soot eventually fell back to the Earth, creating a global rock layer known to geologists as the K-T Boundary. In the long term, carbon dioxide built up in the atmosphere (because there were no more plants to remove it), leading to global warming. The ozone was destroyed from sulfate aerosol formation. It took the Earth's centuries to recover from these long term effects. In the end, somewhere between 50 and 80% of all species living at that time went extinct.

Even small impacts can cause devastation on a local scale. An example is the Tunguska event. On June 30, 1908 at 7:17 am, a 50 meter meteorite exploded 4 miles above the ground in Tunguska, Siberia. No one was near enough to be injured, but observers reported a "deafening bang" and a fiery cloud. The shock wave from the impact broke windows and knocked people off their feet miles away. When people investigated the area later, they found a 25 mile wide area where trees had been burned and flattened radially by the explosion (Figure 12.2). This is about the same size as Washington D.C.

If the meteor at Tunguska had hit the surface, it would have created a crater about 3/4 of a mile in diameter. This is about the size

Figure 12.2: Flattened Trees at Tunguska (https://commons.wikimedia.org/wiki/File:Tunguska_event_fallen_trees.jpg)

of Meteor Crater in Arizona. Meteor Crater was formed 50,000 years ago, in an area that was fortunately probably not inhabited by humans at the time.

However, computer simulations tell us what humans would have experienced had they been there. A fireball would have burned anything within a radius of about 6 miles from the impact. Within 15 miles, large animals would have been killed or wounded from the shockwave. Hurricane force winds would have been experienced up to 25 miles away.

To put this into perspective, let's imagine that such an impact happens in Times Square instead of the Arizona desert (Figure 12.3). A shows the zone that gets burned from the fireball, B shows the zone where large animals are killed or wounded from the shockwave, and C shows the zone that experiences hurricane force winds. The star represents the location of Westchester Community College in Valhalla, NY.

Figure 12.3: Effect of a 50-meter Impactor Hitting Times Square, New York City

We saw that large impacts can cause mass extinctions and global devastation. We also saw that even small impacts can cause a lot of devastation if they hit in the wrong place. Our next question is how often do these events happen? The plot in Figure 12.4 tells us. On the x-axis we have the size of the impact and the corresponding impact energy. Note the scales are logarithmic. On the y-axis we have the recurrence interval. This is the average number of years between impacts of that size. For example, an impact with a recurrence interval of 100 years occurs on average once every 100 years. This does not mean that an impact occurs every 100 years like clockwork; it means that on average in a period of 100 years there was probably one impact. There might have been none, or two, or three, but most likely there was one. Another way to think about this is that each year there is a 1/100, or 1%, chance of an impact this size happening. Reading the chart, we see for example that an impact the size of Chicxulub occurs on average once every 50 million years. This means that each year there is a 1/50 million, or 0.000002%, chance of an impact the size of Chicxulub occurring.

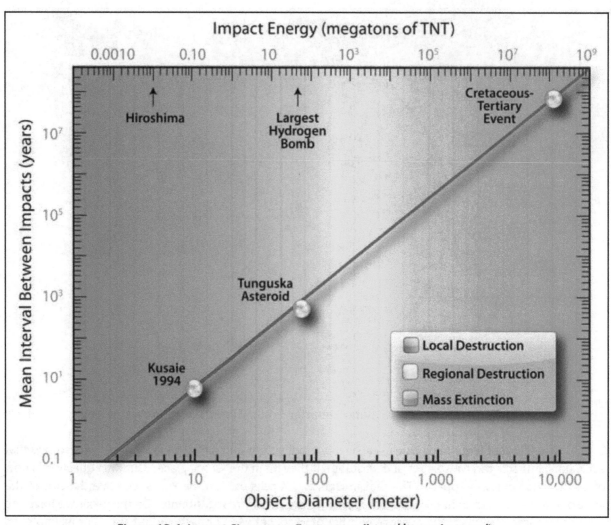

Figure 12.4: Impact Size versus Frequency (http://www.lsst.org/)

An NEO, or Near Earth Object, is an asteroid or comet with an orbit that intersects the Earth's orbit, or passes very near the Earth's orbit, and hence has the potential to hit the Earth. The orbits of all known NEOs (as of early 2013) are shown in Figure 12.5. The orbits of Mercury, Venus, Earth, and Mars are labeled; all other orbits are the orbits of NEOs. As you can see, there are quite a lot.

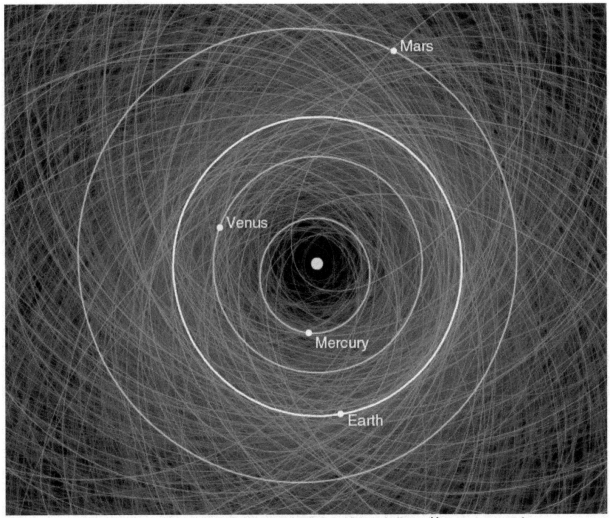

Figure 12.5: The Orbits of Near Earth Objects (NEOs) (http://www.nasa.gov)

Most of these were detected as part of NASA's NEO program. The initial goal of this program was to detect at least 90% of NEOs bigger than 1 km (the threshold for mass extinction) by 2008. So far (as of June 5, 2018) 18,214 NEOS have been discovered. 893 of them have a diameter bigger than 1 km. Since it is estimated there are about 1,000 NEOs with diameters bigger than 1 km, this is almost 90%. Thus the new goal of the program is to detect at least 90% of NEOs greater than 140 m by 2020. So far 8,172 of these have been found.

Which leads us to the question – what do we do if we discover an NEO headed towards us?

The National Research Council recently put together a committee of scientists to analyze this question and create a report (Figure 12.7). They recommended three ways to deflect an asteroid.

The first method is known as the gravity tractor method. In this method, the gravity of a spaceship is used to slowly pull the asteroid off of its current trajectory. It's like a tractor, but the spaceship is not attached. The benefit of this method is that it is very precise. The disadvantage is that the gravitational force between the asteroid and the spaceship is very small, so this method only works if you have decades of time and a relatively small asteroid.

If you have less time or a larger asteroid, you can use a kinetic impactor, where you try to deflect the asteroid by hitting it with something. This is not as precise as the gravity tractor, and there is always the chance that you may break up the impactor into several pieces instead of deflecting it!

For the largest objects, a kinetic impactor will not provide enough energy, and a nuclear denotation will be needed.

Thus actions may involve studying and monitoring the asteroid, a characterization mission to the asteroid, agreements between nations, sheltering and evacuation, the gravity tractor, the kinetic impactor, and the nuclear detonation. The appropriate actions depend on the scale of the event and how much warning time we have. For the smallest scale events, the best action is sheltering and evacuation. For medium and large scale events, if there is little time, sheltering and evacuation is the only option. However, for longer warning times we could try to deflect the asteroid using one of the methods we talked about. The committee also found that some events are so large that there would be inevitable global catastrophe that we don't have the capability to avoid. As you can see, the committee labeled these events as Earths with x's over them.

Scale of Event	Warning Time		
	Short (days-few years)	Medium (few years-decade)	Long (multiple decades)
Small (local/national)			
Medium (regional/multinational)			
Large (global/international)			
Largest (global catastrophe/ unable to avoid)			

	Study and monitor		Civil defense (shelter, evacuation)
	Characterization mission		Slow push orbit change (gravity tractor)
	Bilateral agreements		Kinetic impact
	International agreements/cooperation		Nuclear detonation
			No avoidance capability—global devastation

Figure 12.7: Impact Mitigation Strategies (NRC)

147

Questions You Should Be Able to Answer
1. Describe some of the effects of large and small(er) impact events.
2. What is a recurrence interval?
3. Do large impacts happen more or less frequently than small impacts?
4. What is a NEO? What is the NEO program and what are its goals?
5. What are some of the ways scientists are working on to mitigate the effects of a large impact event?

Suggestions for Further Reading
1. http://neo.jpl.nasa.gov/ (NASA's Near Earth Object Program website)
2. http://www.pbs.org/wgbh/nova/earth/meteor-strike.html (PBS Nova program about the Chelyabinsk Meteor)

Common Pitfalls

-The recurrence interval is a statistical average, not a definitive predictor of what will happen. For example, an impact that has a recurrence interval of 20 years happens on average once every 20 years. So in any given period of 20 years, the most statically likely number of impacts is 1. But there may have been 0 or 2 or even 10!

Chapter 12 Activity: Impact Hazards

Part 1: Dice Rolling

When you roll two die, you can roll anywhere from a (combined) 2 to a 12. The odds of rolling each is:

Number	2	3	4	5	6	7	8	9	10	11	12
Odds	1/36	1/18	1/12	1/9	1/7.2	1/6	1/7.2	1/9	1/12	1/18	1/36
Odds, %	2.8%	5.6%	8.3%	11.1%	13.9%	16.7%	13.9%	11.1%	8.3%	5.6%	2.8%

Below are the results of rolling two dices 100 times (first roll was 8, second roll was 6, etc.).

8 6 6 9 8 10 7 10 7 12 3 9 11 3 7 7 9 11 6 9 7 7 10 9 7 9

10 6 6 3 7 7 4 6 8 8 3 10 6 8 6 10 8 11 9 8 11 7 6 8 6 7

4 7 10 3 7 8 4 6 4 7 6 6 7 6 3 6 5 8 3 2 7 7 7 4 11 7 6

9 8 2 3 4 7 10 4 7 7 9 11 9 9 5 8 3 6 7 7 5

1. Given the calculated odds, how many times would you *expect* to roll a 7 in 100 rolls?

2. How many 7 were *actually* rolled?

The reason that your answers to 1 and 2 don't match exactly is because statistics don't tell you what is going to happen: they just tell you what is *likely* to happen. The more rolls, the closer your answer would be to what is expected!

3. Each roll of the die has a 1/6 chance of adding up to 7. Does this mean that every 6th roll is a 7? Provide evidence to support your answer.

4. Can you roll a 7 more than once in a row?

Dice rolling is a statistically *independent event*. This means that what happens on one roll is irrelevant to what happens on the next roll. The chance of getting a 7 on a roll is always 1/6, no matter how many 7's you've rolled (or haven't rolled) previously!

Part 2: Recurrence Intervals

Many natural disasters (for example floods and meteorite impacts) are statistically independent events as well. Just as the chance of getting a 7 on a roll is always the same, the chance of having a meteorite impact of a certain size is always the same, regardless of what happened previously. We describe the chance of having a meteorite impact of a certain size in terms of the recurrence interval. The recurrence interval is the number of years *on average* between impacts of that size. In the dice rolling analogy, the recurrence interval of getting a 7 would be 6 flips (once every 6 flips).

Suppose that a certain size impact event has a recurrence interval of 100 years (once every 100 years).

5. Does this mean that an impact event this size will happen *exactly* every 100 years?

6. How many of these impacts would you expect to have in a period of 1,000 years?

7. What is the chance of having an impact event this size in any given year?

8. Suppose that you have an impact event this size in 2014. What is the chance of having an impact this size in 2015?

9. **Student 1** says, "Since there was an impact event in 2014, there won't be one again for another 100 years. The next one will be due in 2114, so the chance is 0% in 2015."

Student 2 says, "But what happened in previous years is irrelevant. Each year is statistically independent, so the chance in 2015 is the same as it was in 2014. This is 1/100, which is 1%."

With which student or students do you agree with and why?

Part 2: Impact Hazards

The chart below shows the recurrence intervals for different-sized impact events on the Earth. Use this chart to answer the following questions. Please note that the scales are logarithmic! Plot from http://www.lsst.org/

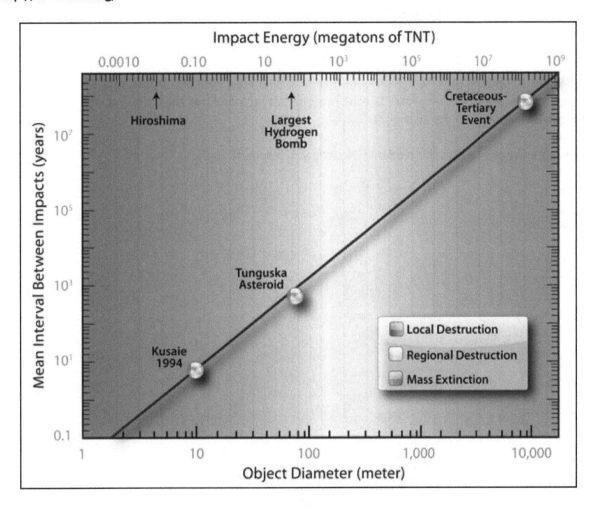

10. On February 15, 2013, a 20 m in diameter meteor exploded in the air over Chelyabinsk, Russia, injuring 1,500 people. How often do events of this size occur?

11. How often do Tunguska-sized impact events occur?

12. How often do Chicxulub-sized (Cretaceous-Tertiary Event) impact events occur?

13. Do large impacts happen more or less frequently than small impacts?

14. The Earth is 4.5 billion years old (4.5*10^9 = 4,500,000,000 years). How many Chicxulub-sized impact events do you think occurred over the Earth's history?

15. Suppose a student says: "Large (greater than 5km diameter) asteroids collide with the Earth on average once every 10 million years - but the most recent recorded was the Chicxulub impact 65 million years ago. We're overdue for an impact!"

Do you agree/disagree with this student? How do you respond?

Chapter 13: The Moon

In this chapter, you will learn about the Moon. We will talk about the exploration, evolution, and formation of the Moon.

Missions to the moon (US)

- Pioneers (1958 and 1959): flybys
- Rangers (1961-1965): crash landers
- Surveyors (1966-1968): soft landers
- Apollo Program (1968-1972): manned missions
- Clementine (1994): orbiter
- Lunar Prospector (1998): orbiter
- Lunar Reconnaissance Orbiter, LRO (2009): orbiter
- Lunar Crater Observation and Sensing Satellite, LCROSS (2009): impactor

Figure 13.1: Missions to the Moon

Missions to the Moon (Figure 13.1) have mostly focused on preparation for the manned lunar missions, the Apollo Program. Since then, there have only been 4 US missions to the Moon.

The Moon is smaller than the Earth; its mass is about 1% the Earth's mass and its radius is about 27% the Earth's radius. Additionally, the Moon's density is significantly smaller than the Earth's density; this implies that the Moon has proportionally less metal than the Earth does. Figure 13.2 show two sides of the Moon; on the left is the side that always faces the Earth (the near side) and on the right is the side that always faces away from the Earth (the far slide). Note that there appears to be two major terrains on the Moon; the darker areas, and the lighter areas.

Figure 13.2: The Moon (http://www.nasa.gov)

If we look at a topographic map of the Moon (Figure 13.3), we can see that the darker areas generally coincide with areas that are lower in elevation. Hence we call them the lowlands, or the maria.

The lighter areas generally coincide with areas that are higher in elevation. Hence we call them the highlands.

Figure 13.3: Topography of the Moon (http://www.nasa.gov, Clementine)

The lowlands have less craters than the highlands, indicating that they are younger. The lowlands are composed of low lying, smooth lava flows, while the highlands are composed of jumbled mountains that were pushed up by large impact cratering events. The lowlands are composed of the igneous rock basalt, which is dark in color. The highlands are composed of the igneous rock anorthosite, which is light in color.

We can put this information together to come up with a sequence for the evolution of the Moon. When the moon first formed 4.6 billion years ago, the entire surface was liquid rock; we call this a magma ocean. From 4.6 to 4.1 billion years ago, differentiation occurred in this magma ocean. Heavy minerals sank to the bottom and lighter minerals rose to the surface. The minerals that rose to the surface solidified, forming the highlands.

This was followed by a period of late heavy bombardment from 4.0 to 3.8 billion years ago. During this time, the cratering rate on the Moon spiked for unknown reasons (Figure 13.4). Giant impact basins, like the Orientale Basin, which is as big as Texas, were formed.

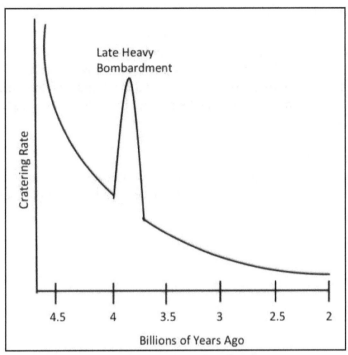

Figure 13.4: Late Heavy Bombardment

The giant impact basins formed during the late heavy bombardment weakened and cracked the crust. From 4 to 2 billion years ago, lava rose up through these cracks and pooled in the impact basins. When the lava cooled, it formed the lowlands.

By about 2 billion years ago, the Moon's interior had cooled sufficiently that the interior was no longer partially molten and volcanism stopped. Since then, the moon has been geologically dead. The only activity now is cratering.

Where did the moon come from in the first place? Following the Apollo missions to the Moon, scientists developed several hypotheses to answer this question. We will discuss the four most popular at the time. The binary accretion hypothesis suggests that the Moon and the Earth formed at the same time from the same cloud of debris. In other words, as a cloud of debris coming together formed the Earth, the outer edges of that cloud came together to form the Moon via the same process. The capture hypothesis suggests that the Moon is an asteroid that drifted too close to the Earth and was captured by the Earth's gravity. The fission hypothesis suggests that the Moon formed when the Earth broke up because it was spinning too fast. Lastly, the giant impact hypothesis suggests that the Moon was formed from material thrown off during a large impact event.

When scientists have several hypotheses, they analyze the available evidence to see which hypothesis is most consistent with that evidence. We will do this together in class to figure out which hypothesis makes the most sense!

Questions You Should Be Able to Answer
1. How does the moon's mass, radius, and density compare to the Earth's?
2. What are the differences between the lunar highlands and lowlands?
3. Describe the evolution of the moon from magma ocean to present day.
4. What are the binary accretion, capture, fission, and giant impact hypotheses for the formation of the moon? Which hypothesis do scientists currently favor? What are the problems with the other hypotheses?

Suggestions for Further Reading
1. http://nineplanets.org/luna.html (Nine Planets Moon page)
2. http://nssdc.gsfc.nasa.gov/planetary/planets/moonpage.html (NASA Moon page)

Chapter 13 Activity: Formation of the Moon

Part A – The competing hypotheses.

1. What is the binary accretion hypothesis for the formation of the moon?

2. What is the capture hypothesis for the formation of the moon?

3. What is the giant impact hypothesis for the formation of the moon?

Part B – The binary accretion hypothesis.

4. What prediction does the binary accretion hypothesis make about the comparative compositions of the Earth and the Moon (same, different)?

5. What prediction does the binary accretion hypothesis make about the tilt of the moon's orbit relative to the Earth's orbit (no relative tilt, tilt)?

Student A says, *"The binary accretion hypothesis says that the Earth and moon formed from the same cloud of debris. So I think this hypothesis predicts that the Earth and moon should have the same composition."*

Student B says, *"But I think that since the Earth is bigger it will have collected more metal and be denser."*

Student A says, *"It doesn't matter how big the planet is if they came from the same cloud of debris. If you put 1 cup of flour and 1 cup of sugar in a bowl and mix them together it doesn't matter if you take a spoonful or a cupful of the mixture...you'll still have the same ratio of flour/sugar. It's the same thing with the cloud of solar system debris."*

With which student(s) do you agree, and why?

Part B – The capture hypothesis.

6. What prediction does the capture hypothesis make about the comparative compositions of the Earth and the Moon (same, different)? Hint: analysis has shown that large asteroids have the same density and volatile content as the Earth.

7. What prediction does the capture hypothesis make about the tilt of the moon's orbit relative to the Earth's orbit (no relative tilt, tilt)?

Part B – The giant impact hypothesis.

8. What prediction does the giant impact hypothesis make about the comparative compositions of the Earth and the Moon (same, different)?

9. What prediction does the giant impact hypothesis make about the tilt of the moon's orbit relative to the Earth's orbit (no relative tilt, tilt)?

Student A says, *"In the giant impact hypothesis, the moon forms from the debris thrown off from the Earth. So I think that this hypothesis predicts that the Earth and the moon should have the same composition."*

Student B says, *"But I think that the impact could change the composition. For example, the impact will heat up the debris, causes any volatiles stored within the rock to be released. Also when the Earth was hit, all of the metal would have been at the center of the Earth, in the core. So the debris will primarily consist of the rock from the mantle and crust."*

With which student(s) do you agree, and why?

Part C – Putting it together.

A good hypothesis for the formation of the moon should be able to explain the major observations about the moon (listed below). Fill in the chart below by stating whether the binary accretion, capture, and giant impact hypotheses are consistent with the observations. Be prepared to explain your reasoning. Hint: Look back at your predictions for each hypothesis. Are the predictions consistent with the evidence?

Observation	Can it be explained by the binary accretion hypothesis? Why or why not?	Can it be explained by the capture hypothesis? Why or why not?	Can it be explained by the giant impact hypothesis? Why or why not?
The moon and the Earth must have formed at similar locations in the solar system.			
The moon is much less dense than the Earth.			
The moon has less volatile (gaseous) elements than the Earth does.			
The moon's orbit is tilted relative to the Earth's orbit.			

Based on the above chart, which hypothesis do you think is more likely to be correct? Why?

Chapter 14: Mercury

In this chapter, you will learn about Mercury. We will talk about the exploration, surface and interior, and history of Mercury.

There have been very few missions to Mercury; one flyby in 1973 (Mariner 10), and more recently, an orbiter that is currently actively collecting data (MESSENGER - Mercury Surface, Space, Environment, Geochemistry, and Ranging Mission).

Mercury is similar in size to the Moon; its mass is about 6% the Earth's mass and its radius is about 38% the Earth's radius. Mercury's density is significantly larger than the Earth's density; this implies that Mercury has proportionally more metal than the Earth does. Figure 14.1 shows a view of Mercury as mapped by MESSENGER.

Mercury is a cratered, airless, and geologically dead world, similar to the Earth's Moon. However, there are some difference between Mercury and the Moon. On the Moon, there are darker areas (the maria, or lowlands). On Mercury, there are terrains of different ages, but they are all the same color (i.e. made of the same rocks). Temperatures on Mercury vary more greatly than on the Moon, from 800 degrees Fahrenheit in sunlight to -280 degrees Fahrenheit in shadow or night. Lastly, Mercury is 60% denser than the Moon, indicating that it has a lot more metal.

Figure 14.1: Mercury
(http://www.nasa.gov, MESSENGER)

There are three basic terrains on Mercury (Figure 14.2). The oldest is the old cratered terrain, which is saturated with craters. Then there is the intercrater terrain, which is less cratered. The youngest terrain is the smooth plains, which has the fewest craters.

Since Mercury is denser than the Earth, this indicates that it has a proportionally larger core than the Earth does. Scientists do not know why this is true; however, our best guess is that a giant impact early on stripped Mercury of some of its rock.

- Old cratered terrain – saturated with craters
- Intercrater terrain – less cratered
- Smooth plains – even less craters

Figure 14.2: Mercury's Terrains
(http://www.nasa.gov, MESSENGER)

Putting this together gives us a possible history of Mercury. First, a giant impact strips Mercury of some of its lower-density rock, creating a small, dense world with a large metallic core. Then the surface cooled, creating the old cratered terrain. Lava flows then created the intercrater plains, and later lava flows created the smooth plains. Lastly, the interior cooled, creating a geologically dead world.

Questions You Should Be Able to Answer
1. How does Mercury's mass, radius, and density compare to the Earth's?
2. How is Mercury similar to and different than the moon?
3. Describe the history of Mercury.
4. What are some of the open (unknown) questions regarding Mercury?

Suggestions for Further Reading
1. http://nineplanets.org/mercury.html (Nine Planets Mercury page)
2. http://nssdc.gsfc.nasa.gov/planetary/planets/mercurypage.html (NASA Mercury page)

Chapter 14 Activity: Mercury's Orbit

The Earth rotates (counterclockwise) once every 24 hours and revolves (counterclockwise) around the Sun once every year (365.25 days). A day is defined as the time it takes for the Sun to go from being directly overhead (noon) and returning to that position (noon the next day).

1. How long is a day on Earth?

2. A circle has 360 degrees. How many degrees does the Earth revolve around the Sun in one day (remember it takes the Earth 365 days to go around the Sun once)?

3. The diagram below shows the Earth's orbit around the Sun. On the diagram, draw the approximate position of the Earth after one day (if position is pretty much the same, write "same").

4. The thick line represents a mountain; at the position shown the Sun is directly overhead the mountain (it is 12:00 noon). On your drawing from question 3, draw in the position of the mountain after Earth has gone one full rotation. Is the sun overhead the mountain again?

Mercury rotates (counterclockwise) once every 59 Earth days and revolves (counterclockwise) around the Sun once every 88 Earth days. This means that for each revolution around the Sun, Mercury rotates one and a half times.

5. When Mercury has undergone one full rotation, how many degrees has it revolved around the Sun? (Hint: When 59 Earth days have passed, Mercury has undergone one full rotation and has revolved a fraction of 59/88=67% of the way around the Sun.)

6. The diagram below shows Mercury's orbit around the Sun. On the diagram, draw the approximate position of Mercury after it has undergone one full rotation. The thick line represents a mountain; at the position shown the Sun is directly overhead the mountain (it is 12:00 noon). On the diagram, also draw in the position of the mountain after Mercury has gone one full rotation.

7. Refer to your diagram from question 6. Is the Sun directly overhead the mountain when Mercury is in the position that you drew?

8. Based on your answer from 7, is a day on Mercury equal to 59 Earth days (the time it takes Mercury to rotate once)?

9. After 88 days, Mercury will have revolved around the Sun once and returned to the initial position indicated in the diagram from question 6. At this time, Mercury will have rotated one

and a half times. Where will the mountain be? What time will it be for an observer who is standing on the mountain?

10. How long is a Mercurian day?

11. Student A says, "Earth rotates once every 24 hours, and a day is 24 hours. Since Mercury rotates once every 59 Earth days, a day on Mercury is 59 Earth days.

Student B says, "But by the time the Earth rotates once, it hasn't gone very far in its path around the Sun, so the sun is overhead the mountain again. It's not the same on Mercury. By the time Mercury has rotated once, it's all the way on the other side of the Sun! So the Sun isn't overhead the mountain again yet, meaning a day must be longer than one rotation. Once Mercury has revolved completely around the Sun, it will be back in its original position. So a day on Mercury is 88 Earth days."

Student C says, "But once Mercury has revolved completely around the Sun, then it will have rotated one and a half times. So the mountain will be pointing away from the Sun, and it will be the middle of the night. It will take two full revolutions for it to be the middle of the day at the mountain again. Thus a day must be 2 x 88 = 176 Earth days.

With which student do you agree and why?

Chapter 15: Venus

In this chapter, you will learn about Venus. We will talk about the exploration, atmosphere, surface, and history of Venus.

There have been several missions to Venus (Figure 15.1). Most have been flybys or orbiters. This is because the surface of Venus is too hot to have a lander or rover operate for more than a few minutes before the equipment is fried (as the single Venera lander discovered!).

Missions to Venus

- Mariner 2, 5, and 10 (1962, 1967, 1973): flybys
- Venera (Soviet Union; 1961-1983): flybys, landers, orbiters
- Pioneer Venus (1978-1992): orbiter
- Magellan (1989-1994): orbiter
- Venus Express (ESA; 2005): orbiter
- Akatsuki (Japan; 2010): orbiter

Figure 15.1: Missions to Venus

Venus is similar in size to the Earth; its mass is about 82% the Earth's mass and its radius is about 95% the Earth's radius. Venus' density is comparable to the Earth's density, and Venus is also the closest planet in distance to the Earth. These similarities initially led scientists to call Venus "Earth's Twin." They (incorrectly!) envisioned a Venus much like the Earth - with water and perhaps life. The picture on the left of Figure 15.2 shows you what you would see if you looked at Venus. The surface is entirely obscured by thick clouds of sulfuric acid. If you looked through the clouds to the surface using radar, you would see the image on the right. Lots of volcanic features would be visible, and there would be relatively few craters compared to the Moon and Mercury.

Figure 15.2: Venus (http://www.nasa.gov, Magellan)

Venus' similarities to Earth quickly end when you get a good look at the planet. Figure 15.3 compares the Venusian atmosphere with the Earth's atmosphere. The Earth's atmosphere is composed primarily of nitrogen and oxygen, while Venus' atmosphere is composed primarily of carbon dioxide. Venus' atmosphere is nearly 100 times thicker than the Earth's atmosphere and is also very dry. Last, the Earth's average temperature at the surface is 60 degrees Fahrenheit; Venus' is 870 degrees Fahrenheit! This is hot enough to melt lead, and makes Venus the hottest planet...even hotter than Mercury!

	Earth	Venus
Composition	Mostly nitrogen and oxygen	Mostly carbon dioxide
Atmospheric pressure	1 atm at surface	90 atm at surface
Water	Wet (1-4% at surface)	Dry (0.002% at surface)
Surface Temperature	Average temperature of ~60 degrees Fahrenheit	Average temperature of ~870 degrees Fahrenheit

Figure 15.3: Comparison of Venus' and Earth's Atmosphere

To understand why Venus is so hot, we need to understand the greenhouse effect, and to understand that, we need to understand a little bit about what light is. Light is an electromagnetic wave. This means that it is a variation in the electric and magnetic fields that travels through space. However, the visible light that you see is only one kind of electromagnetic wave; there are others, like gamma rays and ultraviolet light. The difference between the types of electromagnetic waves is their wavelengths....in order from shortest to longest wavelengths, we have gamma rays, x-rays, ultraviolet rays, visible light, infrared waves, and radio waves (Figure 15.4). The frequency and energy of these waves is inversely proportional to the wavelength, so waves with a longer wavelength have a lower frequency and a lower energy. All types of electromagnetic radiation, however, travel at the same speed (the speed of light).

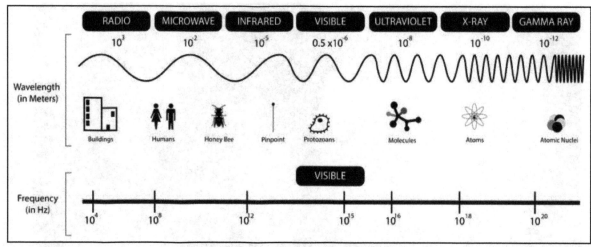

Figure 15.4: The Electromagnetic Spectrum
(https://commons.wikimedia.org/wiki/File:BW_EM_spectrum.png)

All objects absorb and emit electromagnetic radiation, however, they can absorb and emit different wavelengths. For example, your body absorbs visible light but emits infrared light (note that another word for infrared light is heat energy).

Planets do the same thing. Incoming energy from the Sun, which is mostly in the form of visible light, is absorbed by the surface and re-emitted at longer wavelengths, as infrared light. In the absence of the greenhouse effect, this infrared light escapes to space.

Now lets imagine we have a greenhouse as an analogy to how the greenhouse effect works. Glass is transparent to visible light (this is why you can see through a window), so the incoming solar energy is unaffected. However, glass absorbs infrared light (this is why heat doesn't leak out through the glass in windows in the winter), so the outgoing infrared light is trapped. This makes the greenhouse warm.

A greenhouse gas molecule is a gas molecule that behaves like glass: it is transparent to visible light, but absorbs infrared light. Carbon dioxide is an example of a greenhouse gas molecule. So the incoming solar energy is unaffected by the greenhouse gases, but the outgoing infrared light is trapped (Figure 15.5). It is not trapped forever; it will eventually make its way out. However, the more greenhouse gases there are, the longer the infrared light will be trapped, and the hotter the planet will be. Thus Venus is so hot because it has so much carbon dioxide. The reason it has so much carbon dioxide is because it was initially slightly too close to the Sun for liquid water. The Earth, which was slightly further away, had liquid water early on. This water absorbed the carbon dioxide and prevented a runaway greenhouse effect. Since Venus had no liquid water, the carbon dioxide remained, making the planet very hot.

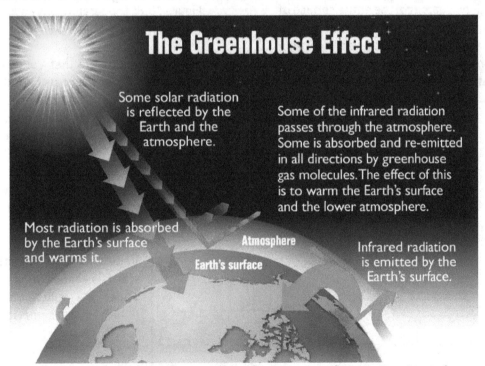

Figure 15.5: The Greenhouse Effect (Environmental Protection Agency)

Let's move to discussing the surface of Venus. Figure 15.6 shows a topographic map of Venus – blacks and dark grays are low elevations and light grays and whites are high elevations. Note that Venus has both smooth, low lying lava plains and highly deformed highlands (called Tesserae). Remember that

when we discussed the Moon and Mercury, both planets had a range of ages on their surfaces; older, cratered areas and younger, less cratered areas. The same is not true for Venus! Anywhere you look on Venus, you will see roughly the same amount of craters. This means the entire surface of Venus is the same age. This age is very young (relative to the age of the solar system), only 500 million years old.

To illustrate how young this is, Figure 15.7 shows the ages of different planetary surfaces. The surfaces of Mercury, the Moon, and Mars are all older than 2 billion years. Only Earth and Venus have younger surfaces. However, even the Earth shows a range of ages. Only Venus shows a surface that is all pretty much all the same age! This is intriguing, and difficult for scientists to explain. It means that 500 million years ago, the entire surface of Venus was molten and cooled all at once. We can't know what happened before then

Figure 15.6: Topography of Venus
(http://www.nasa.gov, Magellan)

(because there is no record preserved). However, some scientists hypothesize that Venus undergoes periodic catastrophic resurfacing, where the surface melts all at once. Other scientists hypothesize that

Venus may have had plate tectonics until a single resurfacing event. We just don't know.

Because Venus is a similar size to the Earth and has active volcanic features, we can infer that it has a similar internal structure, with a molten outer core. However, Venus has no magnetic field, which is confusing. It means that either the outer core is solid (which doesn't make sense) or that the outer core is liquid but doesn't generate a magnetic field. Scientists have suggested that Venus spins too slowly for the liquid in the outer core to create a

Mercury

Moon

Mars

Venus

Earth

Range of Surface Ages (Billions of Years)

Figure 15.7: Planet Surface Ages

magnetic field. This seems like a reasonable solution; however, it is unclear yet how the details of this would work.

We can sum this up into a possible history of Venus. Venus starts by outgassing a thick, carbon dioxide rich atmosphere. Because Venus is slightly too close to the Sun, it is slightly too warm for liquid water. Thus the atmosphere stays around and triggers a runaway greenhouse effect. We have no record of the following 4 billion years, because the entire surface is 500 million years old. Perhaps the planet undergoes period planet-wide overturning of the crust. Perhaps Venus behaved like the Earth (with plate tectonics) until a single recent resurfacing event. Other open questions are why are there no plate tectonics? And how did the tessera form? Venus is clearly a planet with a lot of discoveries left for scientists to figure out!

Questions You Should Be Able to Answer
1. How does Venus' mass, radius, and density compare to the Earth's?
2. How does the atmosphere of Venus differ from the atmosphere of the Earth?
3. Why is Venus so hot? In answering this question, be sure to explain the greenhouse effect.
4. Why is Venus' atmosphere so much thicker than the Earth's?
5. Describe the surface of Venus – how is it similar to and different than the surface of the moon and Mercury?
6. What reasons are there to think that Venus has a molten outer core? What reasons are there to think that Venus' interior is entirely solid?
7. What are some of the unknown questions concerning the history of Venus?

Suggestions for Further Reading
1. http://nineplanets.org/venus.html (Nine Planets Venus page)
2. http://nssdc.gsfc.nasa.gov/planetary/planets/venuspage.html (NASA Venus page)

Common Pitfalls
-Absorbing and emitting light are different from reflecting light. When light is absorbed by a molecule, the electrons in the molecule gain energy and move up energy levels. When light is emitted by a molecule, the electrons in the molecule lose energy and move down energy levels. When light is reflected by a molecule it bounces off the molecule without changing the electons' energy.

Chapter 15 Activity: Greenhouse Effect

Part 1: Electromagnetic Spectrum

The types of light (electromagnetic radiation) differ in wavelength, frequency, and energy. These differences account for difference in the way each type of light interacts with matter. The diagram below shows the all of the types of light on the electromagnetic spectrum (https://commons.wikimedia.org/wiki/File:BW_EM_spectrum.png). Use this for reference to answer questions 1-4.

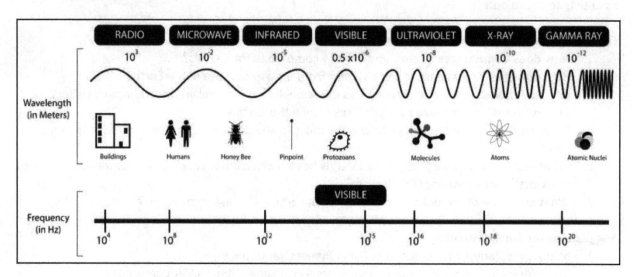

1. Rank the 7 types of electromagnetic radiation from short to long wavelengths. If any are equal, use an equal sign.

2. Rank the 7 types of electromagnetic radiation from low frequency to high frequency. If any are equal, use an equal sign.

3. Rank the 7 types of electromagnetic radiation from high energy to low energy. If any are equal, use an equal sign.

4. Rank the 7 types of electromagnetic radiation from low speed to high speed. If any are equal, use an equal sign.

Part 2: Earth's Energy Budget and the Greenhouse Effect

The diagram below shows how the Earth's energy budget would look if there were no greenhouse gases in the atmosphere. Vis stands for visible light and IR stands for IR light. Questions 5-7 refer to this diagram.

Incoming Solar Energy –
342 W/m²
(Vis and IR)

Reflected by Surface and
Escapes to Space –
24 W/m² (Vis)

Radiated by Surface and
Escapes to Space –
318 W/m² (IR)

Absorbed by Surface –
318 W/m²
(Vis and IR)

Radiated by Surface –
318 W/m²
(IR)

5. How much energy is incoming from the Sun? How much energy is escaping to space? How do these numbers compare?

6. Two things happen to the incoming solar energy – what are these two things? Where does *most* of the incoming solar energy go?

7. In response to the incoming solar energy that is absorbed by the surface, the surface heats up and radiates energy. What kind of energy is radiated and what happens to this energy?

The diagram below shows the Earth's actual energy budget. Note that the effect of greenhouse gases in the atmosphere is included. A greenhouse gas is a gas that is transparent to visible light but absorbs infrared light. Questions 8-16 refer to this diagram.

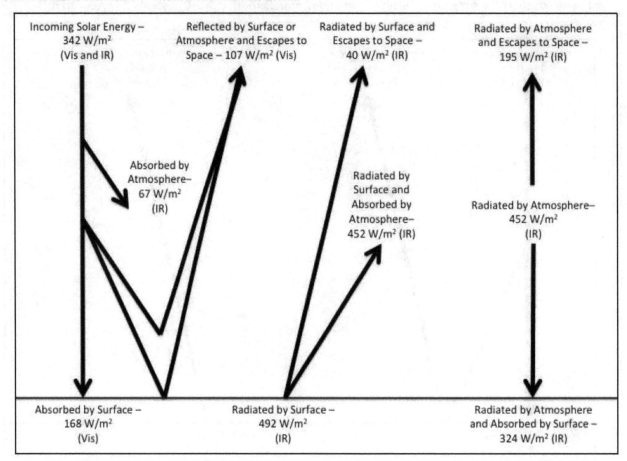

8. How much energy is incoming from the Sun? How much energy is escaping to space? How do these numbers compare?

9. Why are your answers to questions 5 and 8 exactly the same (if they aren't – go back and rethink)?

10. Three things happen to the incoming solar energy – what are these three things? Where does *most* of the incoming solar energy go?

172

11. In response to the incoming solar energy that is absorbed by the surface, the surface heats up and radiates energy. What kind of energy is radiated and what happens to this energy?

12. Note that there are two sources of energy heating the Earth's surface (two arrows going into the surface). What are these two sources? Which source is bigger? What is the total amount of energy going into the surface?

13. How does the total amount of energy going into the surface compare for the case where the atmosphere has no greenhouse gases to where it has greenhouse gases?

14. If the Earth had no greenhouse gases, how would the temperature be different? Explain your reasoning using your answer from question 13.

15. If the Earth had more greenhouse gases than it does, how would the temperature be different? Explain your reasoning using the diagram.

16. Two students are discussing how the greenhouse effect works:

Student A says, *"I get it. Incoming solar energy, which is mostly visible light, is absorbed by the surface. In response, the surface heats up and radiates out infrared energy. Without any greenhouse gases, this energy escapes to space. But when there are greenhouse gases, this energy is permanently trapped, heating up the planet."*

Student B says, *"But I don't think it can be permanently trapped. If you look at the amount of energy incoming versus outgoing, it is always the same regardless of whether or not there are greenhouse gases. I think the greenhouse gases only trap the infared energy temporarily, sending an additional component of energy back to the surface and making it warmer.*

With which student(s) do you agree and why?

17. Explain what is wrong with each student's statement about how the greenhouse effect works below.

a) Student A says, "Greenhouse gases temporarily trap the incoming visible light from the Sun."

b) Student B says, "Greenhouse gases absorb visible light and are transparent to infrared light."

c) Student C says, "Greenhouse gases permanently trap outgoing infrared light from the surface of a planet."

d) Student D says, "The more greenhouse gases a planet has, the colder it will be because greenhouse gases shield the planet from the Sun's light."

e) Student E says, "Greenhouse gases create a hole in the atmosphere, allowing more light to come in and heat the planet."

Chapter 16: Mars

In this chapter, you will learn about Mars. We will talk about the exploration, atmosphere, surface There have been many many missions to Mars, including flybs, orbiters, landers, and rovers (Figure 16.1). Note that about 1/3 of these mission actually failed, for various reasons. This highlights the fact that space missions are not particularly easy!

Missions to Mars

- Mariner 4, 6, 7, and 9 (1964, 1969, 1971): flybys and orbiter (9)
- Mars 2, 3, 5, and 6 (Soviet Union; 1971 and 1973): orbiters and landers
- Viking (1975): orbiters and landers
- Phobos (Soviet Union; 1988): orbiter and lander
- Mars Observer (MO) (1992): orbiter → contact lost three days before orbit insertion
- Mars Pathfinder (1996): lander and rover
- Mars Global Surveyor (MGS) (1996): orbiter
- Mars 96 (Soviet Union; 1996): orbiter, two landers, two impactors → crashed during takeoff
- Nozomi (Japan; 1998): orbiter → failed to go into orbit
- Mars Climate Orbiter (1998): orbiter → lost contact during orbit insertion due to unit conversion failure!!!!
- Deep Space Two (1999): two impactors → contact lost during flight to Mars
- Mars Polar Lander (1999): lander → crashed while attempting to land on Mars
- 2001 Mars Odyssey (2001): orbiter
- Mars Express (ESA; 2003): orbiter and lander (lander failed)
- Mars Exploration Rovers (MER) (2003): rovers (Spirit and Opportunity)
- Mars Reconnaissance Orbiter (2005): orbiter
- Phoenix (2007): lander
- Mars Science Laboratory (2011): rover (Curiosity) currently operating on Mars

Figure 16.1: Missions to Mars

Mars is smaller in size than the Earth; its mass is about 11% the Earth's mass and its radius is about 53% the Earth's radius. However, Mars' density is very similar to the Earth's density. The pictures in Figure 16.2 show you what you would see if you looked at Mars on different days. On the left is a clear day - you can see through the atmosphere to the features on the surface and the ice caps on the poles. The photo on the right was taken during a massive dust storm; wind picked up the dust on the surface and suspended it in the atmosphere, obscuring the view.

June 26, 2001

Hubble Space Telescope • WFPC2

NASA, J. Bell (Cornell), M. Wolff (SSI), and the Hubble Heritage Team (STScI/AURA) • STScI-PRC01-31

September 4, 2001

Figure 16.2: Mars (http://www.nasa.gov, Hubble)

Figure 16.3 compares Mars' atmosphere with the Earth's and Venus' atmospheres. Like Venus' atmosphere, Mars' atmosphere is composed primarily of carbon dioxide. However, while Venus' atmosphere is about 100 times thicker than the Earth's atmosphere, Mars' atmosphere is about 100 times thinner than the Earth's atmosphere. Mars' atmosphere is drier than the Earth's atmosphere, but wetter than Venus' atmosphere. Because Mars' atmosphere is so thin, the greenhouse effect is small, and the planet is very cold - the average temperature is -80 degrees Fahrenheit, much too cold for liquid water to exist. A cup of liquid placed on the surface would quickly freeze and then, because pressures are very low, would sublimate (turn into a gas) in the atmosphere.

	Earth	Venus	Mars
Composition	Mostly nitrogen and oxygen	Mostly carbon dioxide	Mostly carbon dioxide
Atmospheric pressure	1 atm at surface	90 atm at surface	0.006 - 0.01 atm at surface
Water	Wet (1-4% at surface)	Dry (0.002% at surface)	Dry (0.03% at surface)
Surface Temperature	Average temperature of ~60 degrees Fahrenheit	Average temperature of ~870 degrees Fahrenheit	Average temperature of ~-80 degrees Fahrenheit

Figure 16.3: Comparison of Earth's, Venus', and Mars' Atmospheres

Mars atmosphere was probably not always so thin and cold. It is estimated that it was 10-100 times thicker in the past. The gas that used to be in the atmosphere is now stored in the polar caps (which are composed of carbon dioxide ice with water ice underneath), stored as ice under the surface, stored as oxygen locked in rust (this is what makes the planet red), and lost to space.

Figure 16.4 shows a topographic map of Mars; darker gray is low elevation and lighter gray is high elevation. The planet appears divided roughly in half. In the northern area, we have smooth, young plains with few craters. This area is as smooth as the bottom of the Earth's oceans. In the southern area, we have the cratered highlands. There are several shield volcanoes dotting the surface, and a canyon, called Vallas Marineris runs along the equator. This canyon is the largest canyon in the solar system; at 2,500 miles long it would stretch from San Francisco to Boston.

Figure 16.4: Topography of Mars (http://www.nasa.gov, Mars Global Surveyor)

There is abundant evidence that water once flowed over the Martian surface in the form of water carved and deposited features. We can find examples of outflow channels, stream valleys (Figure 16.5 left), and deltas (Figure 16.5 right) all over the surface of Mars.

Figure 16.5: Stream Valley (left) and Delta (right) on Mars (ESA, Mars Express)

Additionally, there are rocks and minerals on the Martian surface that only form in the presence of liquid water. These include hematite spherules (nicknamed "blueberries"), sulfate minerals like jarosite, and sedimentary rocks (Figure 16.7).

If we look at the pattern of stream valleys, all of them appear to flow in the same general direction; downhill, towards the northern hemisphere, where they end. This suggests that the northern hemisphere may have once been filled with an ocean of liquid water. This would also explain the extreme smoothness of the northern plains.

Temperatures on Mars are currently too cold for liquid water. The water that once flowed over the surface in now stored in the polar ice caps, in glaciers, and underneath the surface.

Figure 16.6: Sedimentary Rocks on Mars

(http://www.nasa.gov, MER Opportunity)

Mars has a similar density to the Earth; thus its core/mantle ratio is similar. However, Mars is about half the radius of the Earth. Thus the interior of Mars has cooled and is no longer partially molten. Because of this, there is no magnetic field and no active volcanoes. However, there is evidence that there once was a magnetic field and active volcanoes (Figure 16.7).

Figure 16.7: Inactive Volcano (Olympus Mons) on Mars, and the Largest Volcano in the Solar System
(http://www.nasa.gov)

We can put this together into a history of Mars. Scientists divide Martian history into three distinct periods. The early period, from formation (4.6 billion years ago) to 3.5 billion years ago, is known as the Noachian period. During this period, the Martian atmosphere was thicker. Because it was thicker, there was a stronger greenhouse effect and the planet was warmer. This allowed for liquid water on the surface. During this time the interior was still hot, allowing for abundant volcanic activity and a magnetic field. In other words, during the Noachian period, Mars was a lot like the Earth. The Southern hemisphere of Mars dates from this period.

The next period, from 3.5 to 1.8 billion years ago, is known as the Hesperian period. During this period, the interior cooled. As a result volcanic activity slowly decreased, there was less outgassing, and the magnetic field died. This had a profound effect on the atmosphere because the magnetic field protects the atmosphere. The sun continually gives of streams of charged particles - this is called the solar wind. If a planet has a magnetic field, it will deflect the solar wind safely around it. But without a magnetic field, the solar wind will continually bombard the atmosphere, leading to erosion as atmospheric particles are pushed into space. When Mars lost its magnetic field, its atmosphere began to thin from this process and was no longer replenished, since there was no more outgassing. As the atmosphere thinned, it cooled, and eventually temperatures were too cold for liquid water and any liquid water froze. The Northern hemisphere dates from this period and the next period.

The most recent period of Martian history, from 1.8 billion years ago to present, is known as the Amazonian period. During this period, the atmosphere has been thin and cold. The interior has been cooled, leading to no volcanism and no magnetic field. At this point, Mars is almost dead, with the only active processes being wind erosion and meteorite impacts.

Because Mars was a lot like the Earth at the same time that life was forming on the Earth, many scientists wonder if life ever developed on Mars. The most recent Mars Rover, Curiosity, focused on this question. Curiosity found evidence of hospitable environments on Mars – lakes and streams that were not too salty and not to acidic or basic – just right for life. However, it's important to realize that if life did develop on Mars, it probably only reached the form of bacteria before the planet died (as that is how far along life on Earth got in that time frame), and fossils from bacteria are very difficult to identify, even on the Earth!

Questions You Should Be Able to Answer

1. How does Mars' mass, radius, and density compare to the Earth's?
2. How does the atmosphere of Mars differ from the atmosphere of the Earth and Venus?
3. Give some of the evidence showing that Mars may have had liquid water flowing over its surface in the past.
4. Give some of the evidence showing that Mars may currently have large reservoirs of ice under its surface.
5. Describe the history of Mars. Be sure to indicate the three major periods and give the major events that happened in those eras.
6. What is the name of the current rover exploring the surface of Mars?

Suggestions for Further Reading

1. http://nineplanets.org/mars.html (Nine Planets Mars page)
2. http://nssdc.gsfc.nasa.gov/planetary/planets/marspage.html (NASA Mars page)
3. http://mars.jpl.nasa.gov/ (JPL Mars page)
4. http://www.newyorker.com/magazine/2013/04/22/the-martian-chroniclers (excellent article about Curiosity from the New Yorker)

Chapter 16 Activity: Mars Concept Map

In this activity, we are going to make a concept map of Mars' history. This map will show the relationships between what Mars was like during its three periods: the Noachian Period (early), the Hesperian Period (middle), and the Amazonian Period (late). To make your concept map, follow the steps below to fill in the map on the following page.

STEP 1: Use the phrase list below to fill in the bubbles describing the Noachian Period of Mars' history. Each phrase is used once. Be sure to fill in the bubbles so that the connections and phrases between them make sense.

Phrase List:
thick and warm
magnetic field
hot
liquid water on the surface
greenhouse gases
volcanism

STEP 2: Use the phrase list below to fill in the bubbles describing the Hesperian Period of Mars' history. Each phrase is used once. Be sure to fill in the bubbles so that the connections and phrases between them make sense.

Phrase List:
volcanism decreasing
less greenhouse gases
cooling
water freezing
thin and cold
dying magnetic field

STEP 3: The concept map for the Amazonian Period has not been started. To complete this section, read the paragraph below and draw bubbles and labeled arrows (similar to the previous two periods) to complete your map.

During the Amazonian Period of Martian history, the interior of the planet has been cool, so there is no longer any volcanism and no longer a magnetic field. Since there is no volcanism, there are no greenhouse gases being emitted to replenish the atmosphere. (which has largely been lost because of the lack of a magnetic field to hold it in). As a result the atmosphere is thin and cold. Temperatures are not warm enough for liquid water, so any water on the surface is in the form of ice that is buried under the surface or at the poles.

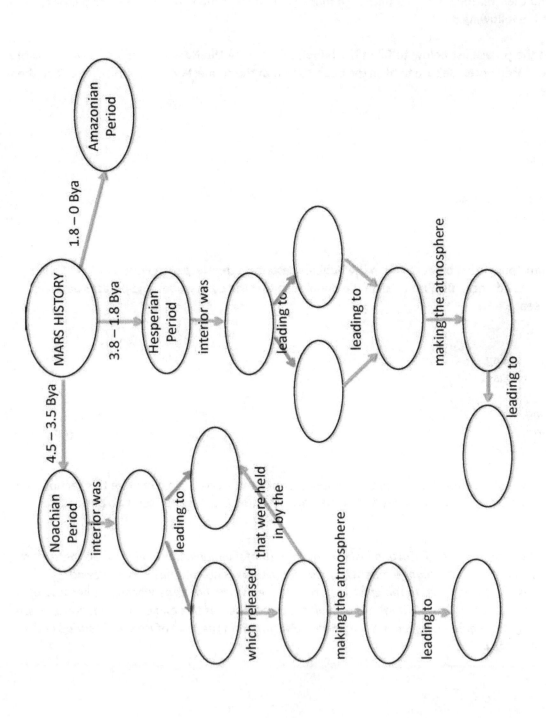

Chapter 16 Activity: Life on Mars

Part 1: Requirements of Life

As far as we know, life needs three main requirements to exist:

-An energy source
-Liquid water
-Chemical building blocks (Oxygen, Carbon, Nitrogen, and Hydrogen)

The chemical building blocks of life are found abundantly throughout the solar system. Which leaves an energy source and liquid water as the remaining requirements for us to examine.

1. What is the energy source that sustains most life on Earth?

2. Is the energy source you identified in question 1 also available on Mars?

3. Does liquid water exist on the surface of Mars today?

4. Did liquid water exist on Mars billions of years ago? How do you know?

5. Circle the features that were forming on Mars billions of years ago.

Volcanoes   Sand Dunes   Stream Beds   Lakes   Craters

6. Circle the features that are forming on Mars today.

Volcanoes   Sand Dunes   Stream Beds   Lakes   Craters

7. How was Mars billions of years ago different from Mars today?

8. Is Mars hospitable to life today?

9. Was Mars hospitable to life billions of years ago?

Part 2: Life on Earth
We saw in part 1 that though Mars does not meet the requirements for life today, it did billions of years ago. In thinking about what kind of life may have developed on Mars, it is useful to think about how life developed on the Earth.

10. On the timescale at the back of this activity, label the following events in the history of life on Earth:

-Carbon isotope evidence of life – 3.8 billion years ago (first evidence of life)
-Oldest fossils – 3.5 billion years ago (simple, single celled bacteria)
-First multi-celled life – 1.5 billion years ago
-Age of Invertebrates – 540-443 million years ago
-Age of Fishes – 443-354 million years ago
-Age of Amphibians – 354-248 million years ago
-Age of Dinosaurs – 248-65 million years ago
-Age of Mammals – 65 million years ago to present day
-Modern day humans – 200,000 years ago (0.2 million years ago)

11. We tend to think of dinosaurs as an ancient from of life on Earth. Is this accurate?

12. On the same timescale, label the following periods of Martian history:

-Noachian – 4.5-3.5 billion years ago
-Hesperian – 3.5-1.8 billion years ago
-Amazonian – 1.8 billion years ago to present day

13. Suppose that one day scientists do find evidence of past life on Mars. What kind of life would you expect this to be? Explain your reasoning.

In this chapter, you will learn about the Jovian planets. We will talk about the exploration, atmospheres, and interiors of these planets.

There have been relatively few missions to the outer solar system: Pioneer 10 and 11 and Voyager 1 and 2 performed flybys of Jupiter Saturn, Neptune, and their moons. Galileo orbited Jupiter, and Cassini orbited Saturn.

Missions to Jupiter, Saturn, Uranus, and Neptune

- Pioneer 10 and 11 (1973 and 1974): flybys of Jupiter

- Voyager 1 and 2 (1977-present day): flybys of Jupiter, Saturn, Neptune, and "beyond"

- Galileo (1989-1995): orbiter and probe to Jupiter

- Cassini (NASA/ESA joint mission; 1997-present day): orbiter to Saturn and probe to Titan

---

Figure 17.1: Missions to the Outer Solar System

Jupiter is much larger in size than the Earth; its mass is 318 times the Earth's mass and its radius is about 11 times the Earth's radius. Jupiter's density is much smaller than the Earth's density. This is because it is a Jovian planet, and is made mostly of gaseous elements (hydrogen and helium) and ice. When you look at Jupiter, you see clouds bands in a turbulent, churning atmosphere (Figure 17.2). To give you some size perspective, Figure 17.3 shows the Earth and Jupiter to scale. The Earth is about as big as the large swirling dot, which is known as Jupiter's "Great Red Spot."

Jupiter's atmosphere is composed primarily of hydrogen and helium (roughly 90% hydrogen and 10% helium with small amounts of other compounds). The different colors you see correspond to different cloud layers. Ammonia clouds are yellowish orange in color, ammonium hydrosulfide clouds are orangish red in color, and water vapor clouds are white in color. The banded pattern of the clouds is known as the belt-zone circulation and is created by the rapid rotation of the winds; Jupiter rotates once every 10 hours. The great red spot is a long-lived hurricane like storm which has been visible since Galileo first observed it 400 years ago.

Shown in Figure 17.4 is a cross-section through Jupiter's atmosphere. Altitude is shown on the y-axis, and temperature is shown on the x-axis (ignore the Uranus line for now). Note that since

Figure 17.2: Jupiter
(http://www.nasa.gov, Voyager)

Figure 17.3: Jupiter (http://www.nasa.gov, Voyager) with the Earth to Scale

Jupiter has no solid surface, 0 altitude has no meaning and is randomly defined. Deep in the atmosphere, temperatures are hot enough that everything is a gas. As you go up, the temperature cools. When you hit 273 Kelvin, water ice condenses out into clouds. When you hit 200 Kelvin, ammonium hydrosulfide ice condenses out into clouds. When you hit 130 Kelvin, ammonia ice condenses out into clouds. Above that there is a haze layer where the atmosphere is filled with dust particles, creating a hazy smog.

What about the interior of Jupiter? There are a few clues. The first is that Jupiter has a very strong magnetic field; it is 14 times larger than the Earth's field at the surface. Something in the interior must be generating this field. Second, the density of Jupiter constrains the rocky/metallic core to 1-10 Earth masses. This seems large, until you remember than the entire planet is 318 Earth masses. Third, Jupiter's radius at the equator is larger than its radius at the poles; it is slightly fat in the middle. This oblateness indicates that the interior is largely liquid. Fourth, we can use mathematic models to learn about Jupiter's interior.

Let's imagine that you could parachute through Jupiter's atmosphere. Jupiter's temperature and pressure are beyond what is known as the critical point of hydrogen. This means there is no distinction between the gaseous and liquid states. Thus, as you parachuted, the atmosphere around you would gradually get thicker and thicker. Eventually you would look around and realize that you are in a liquid; but there would have been no abrupt transition or splashdown. A quarter of the way to the center, the liquid hydrogen would transition into liquid metallic hydrogen. This means that the electrons in the hydrogen atoms are free to float from atom to atom,

Figure 17.4: Cross-Section Through Jupiter's Atmosphere

like in a metal. The liquid metallic hydrogen thus acts exactly like a metal, and this generates a very strong magnetic field, which is about 20 times stronger than the Earth's. By the time you reach the center of Jupiter, the temperature would be 5 or 6 times hotter than the Sun!

Jupiter's structure is illustrated in Figure 17.5 diagram (which also has the structure of the Earth to scale for comparison). We have the cloud tops, the gaseous hydrogen atmosphere, the liquid hydrogen, the liquid metallic hydrogen, and a rocky/metallic core at the center. Note that it is a misnomer to call Jupiter a gas giant - as you can see, it is mostly liquid!

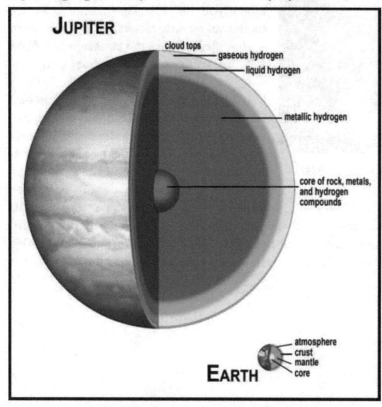

Figure 17.5: Interior Structure of Jupiter

Jupiter has rings, but they are difficult to see, and can only be seen when the planet is lit from behind. The rings are composed of rocky, microscopic particles.

Saturn is much larger in size than the Earth and is similar in size to Jupiter; its mass is 95 times the Earth's mass and its radius is about 9 times the Earth's radius (Figure 17.6).

While Saturn is similar to Jupiter, there are a few significant differences. The first is that Saturn is somewhat smaller, about 1/3 the size of Jupiter. This leads to a weaker magnetic field, since there is not as much liquid metallic hydrogen. Second, Saturn's belt-zone circulation is not as well-defined; it looks "smoother" in images. This is because Saturn is smaller and colder; thus, the cloud layers form deeper down under the haze layer and are harder to see. Third, Saturn's rings are much more prominent than Jupiter's.

Saturn's rings are mostly composed of particles of ice that range in size from dust to small moons. There are dramatic gaps in the rings. To understand why Saturn's rings are so different from Jupiter's rings, we need to understand where the rings come from. Scientists initially thought that the rings were leftovers from solar system formation. However, this would not explain why Jupiter has only faint rings. Furthermore, computer simulations show that rings should clear out in 10 to 100 million years, much shorter than the age of the solar system.

We now think that rings are created in one of two ways. Either a moon gets too close to a planet, and the planet's gravity rips it apart...or, two moons collide and rip each other apart. The resulting debris becomes a ring. Thus Saturn has prominent rings because one of these two events must have happened relatively recently.

A final feature that we see on Jupiter and Saturn is auroras. Auroras are patterns of light that you can see at the north and south poles of a planet; we have them on Earth (Figure 17.7). Auroras are created when solar wind from the Sun is funneled to the poles by the planet's magnetic field. As the solar wind particles come in at the poles,

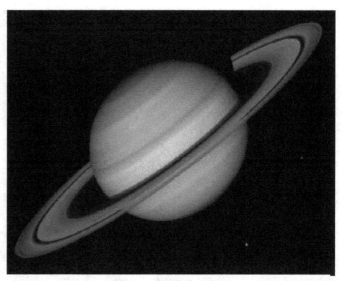

Figure 17.6: Saturn

they collide with molecules in the atmosphere. The collisions release energy in the form of light.

Uranus and Neptune are very similar to each other. Both are larger in size than the Earth, but smaller than Jupiter; Uranus' mass is 14 times the Earth's mass, but only 5% of Jupiter's mass. Its radius is about 4 times the Earth's radius. When you look at Uranus, you see a featureless blue ball. Neptune's mass is 17 times the Earth's mass, and its radius is about 4 times the Earth's radius. When you look at Neptune, you see a blue ball with some faint banding (Figure 17.8).

Figure 17.7: Auroras at the Earth's North Pole
(http://image.gsfc.nasa.gov/)

Uranus and Neptune are similar to Jupiter and Saturn with a few notable differences. The first is color. Jupiter and Saturn are orangish-red, while Uranus and Neptune are blue. This is because different cloud layers are visible. When you look at Jupiter and Saturn, what you are seeing are clouds of ammonia, ammonium hydrosulfide, and water. When you look at Uranus and Neptune, what you are seeing is clouds of methane. Second, Uranus and Neptune are relatively featureless. This is not because there are no wind bands; there are. However, because there is only one cloud layer visible, you can't see the wind bands. Third, Uranus and Neptune have very weak magnetic fields (weaker even than the Earth's). Both have rings, but they are faint (like Jupiter's).

Figure 17.8: Uranus (left) and Neptune (right)

The reason that Uranus and Neptune have weak magnetic fields is because they are smaller. Since they are smaller, their interiors never reach the high pressures and temperatures required for liquid metallic hydrogen. Their magnetic fields are instead generated by dissolved ions moving around in liquid water near the surface. This is a very weak source of a magnetic field. Figure 17.9 compares the interiors of all of the Jovian planets. Uranus has a thick envelope of gaseous hydrogen and helium, then a layer of liquid ice and rock, and heavy element core at the center.

Figure 17.9: Interiors of the Jovian Planets (http://www.nasa.gov)

Questions You Should Be Able to Answer
1. How does Jupiter's mass, radius, and density compare to the Earth's?
2. How does the atmosphere of Jupiter differ from the atmosphere of the Earth?
3. Describe the interior of Jupiter and how scientists know anything about it.
4. How does Saturn's mass, radius, and density compare to the Earth's and to Jupiter's?
5. Give some similarities and differences between Jupiter and Saturn.
6. Why is Saturn's magnetic field weaker than Jupiter's magnetic field?
7. Why is wind banding less prominent on Saturn than on Jupiter?
8. Why are Saturn's rings so much more prominent than Jupiter's rings?
9. Explain what creates wind bands, auroras, rings, and spots (like the Great Red Spot of Jupiter).
10. How does Uranus' and Neptune's mass, radius, and density compare to the Earth's and to Jupiter's?
11. Why are Uranus and Neptune blue in color?
12. Why are Uranus' and Neptune's atmospheres relatively featureless (compared to Saturn's and Jupiter's atmosphere's)?
13. Why are the magnetic fields of Uranus and Neptune so weak?

Suggestions for Further Reading
1. http://nineplanets.org/jupiter.html (Nine Planets Jupiter page)
2. http://nineplanets.org/saturn.html (Nine Planets Saturn page)
3. http://nineplanets.org/uranus.html (Nine Planets Uranus page)

4. http://nineplanets.org/neptune.html (Nine Planets Neptune page)
5. http://nssdc.gsfc.nasa.gov/planetary/planets/jupiterpage.html (NASA Jupiter page)
6. http://nssdc.gsfc.nasa.gov/planetary/planets/saturnpage.html (NASA Saturn page)
7. http://nssdc.gsfc.nasa.gov/planetary/planets/uranuspage.html (NASA Uranus page)
8. http://nssdc.gsfc.nasa.gov/planetary/planets/neptunepage.html (NASA Neptune page)

Chapter 17 Activity: Clouds on the Outer Planets

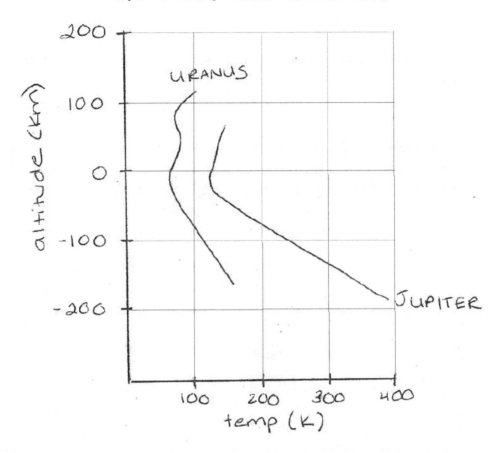

The above plot show the temperature profiles through the atmospheres of Jupiter and Uranus. On the horizontal axis is temperature in Kelvin, and on the vertical axis is altitude (height through the atmosphere) in kilometers. There are two lines – one for Uranus and one for Jupiter. Note that negative heights are below the "surface" and positive heights are above the "surface" (there is no real solid surface; the "surface" is defined as the point where the atmospheric pressure is the same as on the surface of the Earth!)

Considering this graph, answer the following questions:

1. Which planet is warmer? How do you know?

2. What is the temperature at the "surface" of Jupiter?

3. What is the temperature at the "surface" of Uranus?

4. At what altitude does Jupiter reach a temperature of 300 K?

5. At what altitude would you expect Uranus to reach a temperature of 300 K (you will need to extrapolate)?

6. Different gases condense out to form clouds at different temperatures. The chart below lists the temperatures at which gases common to Jupiter and Uranus condense out. Fill in the altitudes at which you would expect these clouds to form for each planet. Note: You can extrapolate the temperature line down (into the atmosphere), but not up (because that is the top of the atmosphere). Methane on Uranus is done for you as an example.

	Condensation Temperature	Altitude of Clouds on Jupiter	Altitude of Clouds on Uranus
Methane	~90 Kelvin		-60 km
Ammonia	~130 Kelvin		
Ammonium hydrosulfide	~200 Kelvin		
Water	~270 Kelvin		

7. The diagram on the next page shows cross-sections through the atmospheres of Jupiter and Uranus. On this diagram, sketch in and label the locations of the cloud layers from question 6. Methane on Uranus is done for you as an example.

194

8. On Jupiter, three cloud layers are easily observed. Which are they?

9. Why don't we observe methane clouds on Jupiter?

10. Ammonia, Ammonium hydrosulfide, and water clouds are not observed on Uranus. Why?

11. *Student A says, "Ammonia, Ammonium hydrosulfide, and water clouds are not observed on Uranus because there is none of those gases there! If those gases aren't found there, they can't condense out to form clouds.*

    Student B says, "But the composition of Jupiter and Uranus are very similar. I think the clouds are there, they are just too deep to see."

    With which student do you agree and why?

12. Suppose that you were observing a Jovian planet that was colder than Uranus. Would you expect its clouds to form deeper down in the atmosphere, higher up in the atmosphere, or at the same height in the atmosphere as the clouds on Uranus? Provide a reasoning for your answer.

13. The dashed line on the graph above shows a hypothetical planet that is colder than Uranus. Determine which clouds would form in the atmosphere of this planet and indicate the altitudes that they would form at.

14. Does your answer from 13 agree with your answer from 12? If not, consider revising your answers.

Chapter 18: Outer Solar System Satellites

In this chapter, you will learn about the moons of the outer solar system. We will talk specifically about the large moons of Jupiter and Saturn.

Figure 18.1 lists the number of moons each planet has, as well as some of their names. The terrestrial planets have few moons; Mercury and Venus have none, the Earth has one, and Mars has two. However, the Jovian planets have many moons; Jupiter has 62, Saturn has 33, Uranus has 27, and Neptune has 13. Notice the interesting naming conventions of these moons. Most are named after characters from Greek and Roman mythology: Jupiter's moons are named after Jupiter's/Zeus' mortal lovers, Saturn's moons are named after the Titans and characters related to the Titans, and Neptune's moons are named after characters related to Neptune/Poseidon. The oddball out is Uranus, whose moons are named after Shakespeare characters!

PLANET	NUMBER OF MOONS	SOME OF THE NAMES
Mercury	0	
Venus	0	
Earth	1	Moon
Mars	2	Phobos, Deimos
Jupiter	62	Io, Europa, Ganymede, Callisto,, Amalthea, Himalia, Elara, Pasiphae, Sinope, Lysithea
Saturn	33	Titan, Rhea, Iapetus, Dione, Tethys, Prometheus, Pandora, Phoebe, Enceladus, Mimas
Uranus	27	Cordelia, Ophelia, Bianca, Cressida, Desdemona, Juliet, Portia, Rosalind, Belinda, Puck
Neptune	13	Triton, Nereid, Naiad, Thalassa, Despina, Galatea, Larissa, Proteus

Figure 18.1: Moons In our Solar System

Selected moons are shown to scale in Figure 18.2. The largest moons are about the size of the Earth's moon. This may seem surprising: you might think that since Jupiter is bigger, that it would have larger moons. The reason behind this is probably the formation mechanism. The moons of the Jovian planets are thought to have formed via binary accretion and the moons of Mars are thought to be captured asteroids. Thus the Earth's moon is so big relative to its planet because it is the only one formed from a giant impact. Jupiter has four large moons, Saturn has one large moon, and the rest of the moons are fairly small. We will talk specifically about each of the large moons.

However, before we do, we should note that the moons are shaped by the same things the Earth and other Terrestrial planets are. Things like impact cratering, volcanism, wind, plate tectonics, and water.

Figure 18.2: Selected Moons of the Solar System to Scale
(https://commons.wikimedia.org/wiki/File:Moons_of_solar_system_v7.jpg)

Additionally, there are two processes that operate on these moons that do not operate on the Terrestrial planets. The first is that strong tides can cause a hot, molten interior, even on a small moon. The second is that liquids other than water can occur on moons that are too cold for liquid water.

Figure 18.3 shows a diagram to help you understand how tides can cause a hot, molten interior. In the diagram, we have a moon orbiting around Jupiter (note that the diagram is not to scale). The pull of Jupiter's gravity on the moon is shown with the black arrows; a longer arrow represents a greater pull. Jupiter's gravity pulls the moon towards it. Because the side of the moon that is facing Jupiter is pulled more than the side of the moon facing away from Jupiter (this is because it is closer, and gravity is stronger when objects are closer), this stretches the moon out into an oval shape. Additionally, since the moon's orbit is elliptical, sometimes it is closer to Jupiter and sometimes it is further. When it is closer, it is more stretched out. When it is further, it is less stretched out. Thus as the moon orbits Jupiter, it repeatedly goes from being less to more stretched out; this is analogous to pulling a rubber band back and forth. This motion will generate friction that heats the planet (just like the rubber band gets hot). If the friction generated is enough, it can even melt the interior and cause volcanoes!

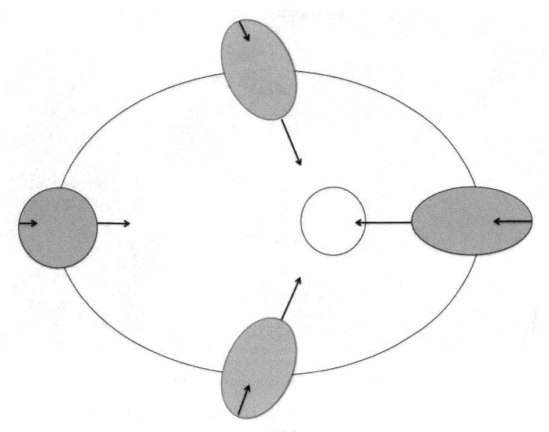

Figure 18.3: Tidal Heating

Titan is Saturn's large moon. When you look at Titan, you can't see through the atmosphere to the surface because it has a very thick nitrogen atmosphere. The surface is composed of frozen water ice and frozen methane. The methane on Titan acts like water on the Earth. It evaporates off the surface, forms clouds, and rains back down onto the surface where it pools in rivers and lakes. There are few craters on the surface because of this. We know that life on Earth needs liquid water to survive; however, many scientists wonder if liquid methane on Titan could substitute for liquid water. Thus Titan is a good place to look for evidence of life.

TITAN IMAGE COURTESY OF NASA JPL

Figure 18.4: Surface of Titan Showing Rivers of Liquid Methane and a Possible Ocean/Lake
(http://www.nasa.gov, Huygens Probe)

Jupiter has four large moons. They are Io, Europa, Ganymede, and Callisto. Though they are all very similar in size (about the same size as the Earth's moon), we are going to see that they are very very different.

Figure 18.5: Callisto
(http://www.nasa.gov, Voyager)

Let's start with Callisto. Callisto has a density of 1800 kg/m^3. This indicates that it is made of ice and rock. When you look at Callisto, you see an old cratered surface. There are darker and lighter areas. The darker areas are dirty ice, and the lighter areas are where recent impacts have exposed cleaner ice that lies beneath. The longer ice sits on the surface of the moon, the dirtier it will get because the ice will sublimate away, leaving dirt behind.

Callisto's interior is uniform and undifferentiated. This means that the ice and rock is all mixed homogenously together; it is not divided into layers.

In contrast, the other large moons of Jupiter are differentiated (Figure 18.6). Both Europa and Ganymede have icy surfaces, followed by a layer of liquid water, followed by a rocky mantle, followed by a metallic core at the center. Io has no water (frozen or liquid) - just a rocky mantle and a metallic core. The reason for these differences has to do with the moons' distances to Jupiter. The closer a moon is to Jupiter, the more tidal heating it will experience. Callisto is the furthest from Jupiter, so tidal heating is insignificant. Thus Callisto never got hot enough to differentiate. Ganymede is second furthest, and then Europa. Both of these moons experienced enough tidal heating to cause them to differentiate and to melt the liquid water into subsurface oceans. Io is the closest to Jupiter and so experiences the most tidal heating. The tidal heating on Io is so strong that it caused Io to differentiate, boiled the liquid water away, and melted some of the rocks in the interior, giving Io a hot, molten interior.

Ganymede has an icy surface composed of darker, older terrain, and brighter, younger terrain (Figure 18.7). There are cracks in the younger terrain where water from the ocean underneath welled up and flooded the surface. Salts have been detected on the surface, indicating that the ocean is salty. The ocean is estimated to be 3 miles thick and 110 miles below the surface.

Europa is similar to Ganymede. However, there is no darker, older terrain. All of the surface is young (Figure 18.8); this is because Europa's ocean is closer to the surface than Ganymede's; it is estimated to be 100 miles thick and 10 miles below the surface. Thus upwelling through cracks occurs more often. Recent measurements have found that Europa intriguingly has a thin, oxygen atmosphere. Its origin is unknown, but it is intriguing because we know that it is life (particularly photosynthetic organisms) that is the source of Earth's oxygen.
Life exists at the bottom of the Earth's

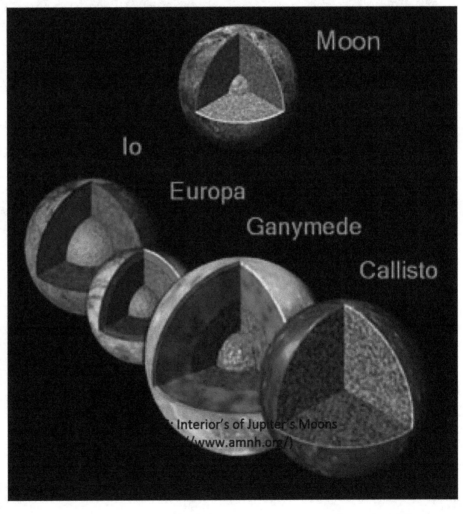

Interior's of Jupiter's Moons
(www.amnh.org/)

oceans, where no sunlight reaches; this life receives its energy from volcanic vents that release heat. Scientists hypothesize that similar vents should exist on the bottom of Europa's ocean, which makes Europa another good place to look for evidence of life.

Figure 18.7: Ganymede
(http://www.nasa.gov, Voyager)

Figure 18.8: Europa
(http://ww.nasa.gov, Voyager)

Io is the driest and most geologically active body in the entire solar system. The tides on Io are so strong that the surface rises and falls by 330 feet each Io day (which is 1.8 Earth days). This generates so much molten rock in the interior that volcanoes on Io are ubiquitous. We have pictures of volcanoes erupting (there are two in the image in Figure 18.9), of lava flowing on the surface (Figure 18.10), and of the gases and dust released by these volcanoes. Eruptions on Io are so frequent that not a single impact crater has been found.

Figure 18.9: Io
(http://www.nasa.gov, New Horizons)

Figure 18.10: Lava on Io
(http://www.nasa.gov, Galileo)

Questions You Should Be Able to Answer

1. What geologic processes shape the moons of the outer solar system?
2. What is tidal heating?
3. Describe the characteristics of Titan.
4. How are measurements of a planet's moment of inertia useful in determining a planet's interior structure?
5. Describe the surfaces and interiors of Io, Europa, Ganymede, and Callisto. Explain what factors cause the extreme differences.

Suggestions for Further Reading

1. http://nineplanets.org/io.html (Nine Planets Io page)
2. http://nineplanets.org/europa.html (Nine Planets Europa page)
3. http://nineplanets.org/ganymede.html (Nine Planets Ganymede page)
4. http://nineplanets.org/callisto.html (Nine Planets Callisto page)
5. http://nineplanets.org/titan.html (Nine Planets Titan page)
6. http://www.astro.washington.edu/users/smith/Astro150/Tutorials/TidalHeat/ (Tidal Heating Explained)

Chapter 14 Activity: Planetary Interiors

Moment of inertia is the resistance of an object to spinning. Measurements of moment of inertia provide more information about a planet's interior structure than density alone. The moment of inertia of a sphere is calculated as $MoI = C * M * R^2$. M is mass and R is radius. C is the "moment of inertia coefficient" and is a reflection of how centrally located a planet is. The lower C is, the lower the moment of inertia, the lower the resistance to spinning, and the MORE centrally located the planet is (e.g. more mass concentrated towards the center). For a completely uniform sphere, C is 0.4.

1. For the two planets in the chart below, please circle the appropriate responses. <u>Both planets have the same mass and radius</u>. Black represents a high metallic density and gray represents a low rocky density.

mass more/less (circle one) centrally located than a uniform sphere	mass more/less (circle one) centrally located than a uniform sphere
more/less (circle one) resistance to spinning than a uniform sphere	more/less (circle one) resistance to spinning than a uniform sphere
higher/lower moment of inertia than a uniform sphere	higher/lower moment of inertia than a uniform sphere
C less than/equal to/greater than (circle one) 0.4	C less than/equal to/greater than (circle one) 0.4

2. The planets in the chart below all have the same mass and radius (e.g. so they have the same amount of rock and metal, but in A the planet is differentiated, and in C it is not). Black represents a higher metallic density and gray represents a lower rocky/metallic mixed density. Order the planets in terms of highest to lowest moment of inertia. Explain your answer!

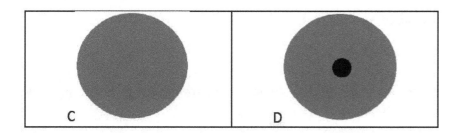

3. Student 1 says, "I think when the core is larger the planet has a harder time spinning so the moment of inertia is higher."
Student 2 says, "No, I think that the larger the core is, the more mass that is centrally located, because more of the heavy metal has been brought to the center. Thus it will be easier to spin and the moment of inertia will be lower. Another way to think about it is that the smaller a planet's core is, the closer it is to uniform. Thus the closer C will be to 0.4."

With which student or students do you agree with and why?

4. Ganymede and Callisto are similar in size and mass, yet they have different moments of inertia (C shown below). Provide an explanation for the differences in C!

Galilean Satellite	C (Moment of Inertia Coefficient)
Ganymede	0.311
Callisto	0.359

Chapter 18 Activity: Tidal Heating

Part 1: Tidal Heating Basics

The diagram below shows Jupiter and two blobs of rock (A and B) that are initially at rest. An arrow showing the pull of gravity on blob A due to Jupiter is drawn.

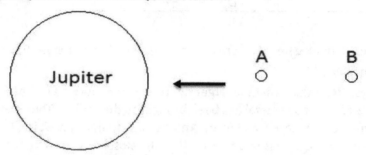

1. Draw an arrow showing the pull of gravity on blob B due to Jupiter. Draw the arrow longer if the force is greater and shorter if the force is smaller!

2. Because of the pull of gravity, the blobs are going to move towards Jupiter. If the pull is greater the blob will move faster. Which blob will move faster - A or B?

3. As the blobs move towards Jupiter will the distance between them get bigger, get smaller, or stay the same?

4. If there was a rubber band connecting the blobs, what would happen to the rubber band as the blobs move towards Jupiter?

Now imagine that A and B are not two separate blobs, but are two different sides of a moon orbiting Jupiter. In this case, since different parts of the moon experience different forces of gravity, the moon's shape will become deformed, as shown.

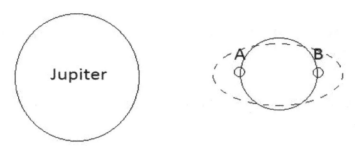

The diagram below shows the orbit of Io around Jupiter. Note that Io's orbit is elliptical, and that Io's orbital period is exactly the same as its rotational period (so that the same side of Io always faces Jupiter, just like the Earth's moon). The distortion of Io at two points in orbit is shown; note that when Io is closer to Jupiter, the distortion is more since the gravitational forces are higher. The location of two points, points A and B, are marked in both diagrams.

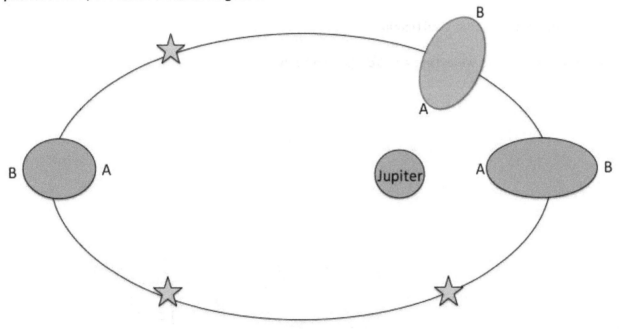

5. Draw Io at the points marked by stars and label positions A and B. Hint: make sure that A is always facing Jupiter, and be sure to draw Io so that it is deformed towards Jupiter.

6. Going back to the rubber band analogy, if there was a rubber band connecting points A and B, what would happen to the rubber band as it goes around Jupiter?

7. If you pull a rubber band back and forth quickly enough, what will happen to the temperature of the rubber band?

8. What do you think will happen to the internal temperature of Io as it goes around Jupiter?

9. Io is the same size as the Earth's moon, yet it has a hot partially molten interior and active volcanoes. Why?

This effect is known as tidal heating; as Io orbits Jupiter, differing gravitational forces cause the surface to rise and fall by about 300 feet each orbit. This deformation generates heat due to friction; enough heat to keep the interior of Io partially molten despite its small size!

Part 2: Factors Controlling Tidal Heating

Suppose that Io's orbit were a perfect circle (shown below).

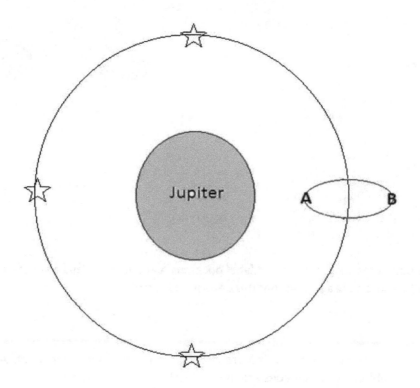

10. Draw Io at the points marked by stars and label positions A and B.

11. If Io's orbit were a perfect circle, do you think Io would experience tidal heating?

12. Two students are discussing their answers to the previous question. With which student(s) do you agree and why?

Student A says, *"I think that since the shape of Io is still distorted, it would still experience tidal heating."*

Student B says, *"But I don't think it is the distortion that matters, I think that is the change from being less distorted to more distorted. Go back to the rubber band analogy. In this case, if point A and B are connected by a rubber band, the rubber band doesn't change shape as it goes around the Jupiter. It just remains spread out. So if it's not going back and forth, it's not going to get hot."*

13. In general, as the eccentricity of a moon's orbit gets larger, does the amount of tidal heating increase or decrease?

Other important factors that affect the amount of tidal heating are the size of the planet (bigger planets exert a larger gravitational pull, which leads to more tidal heating), the size of the moon (bigger moons have a greater difference in gravity between opposite sides, which leads to more tidal heating) and distance (the pull of gravity lessens with distance, which leads to less tidal heating).

14. For *each row* in the chart below, circle the moon that will experience the greatest tidal heating. Give a reasoning for your answer.

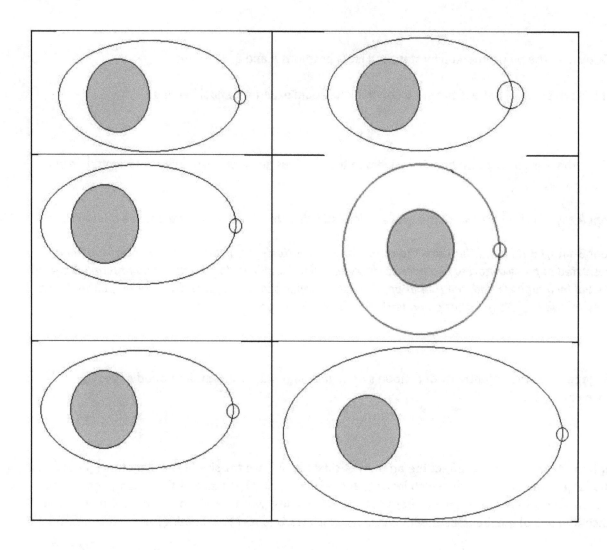

15. Rank the four moons below in terms of the amount of tidal heating that they will experience from greatest to least.

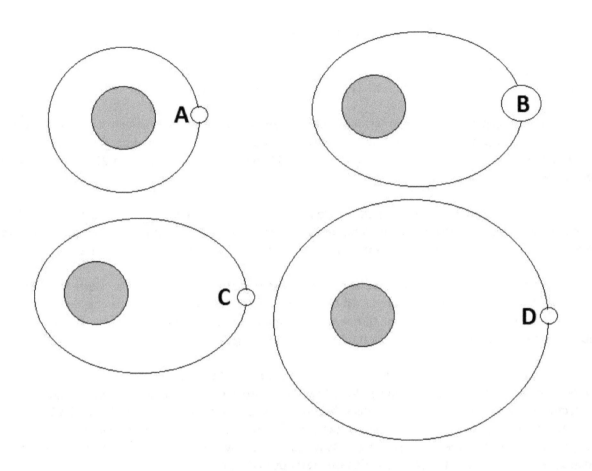

Chapter 19: Detecting Exoplanets

In this chapter, you will learn about the methods that scientists use to find exoplanets (also known as extrasolar planets). We will talk specifically about the radial velocity and transit methods.

An exoplanet is a planet the orbits a star other than our Sun. This is a relatively new field of study. The first exoplanet was discovered in 1989, but we did not begin to find them in abundance until the turn of the millennium. As of June 6, 2018, there were 2950 confirmed exoplanets and 2337 unconfirmed candidates.

Finding exoplanets, particularly Earth-sized exoplanets, is not an easy task. Imagine a basketball on the Moon. Then imagine a grain of sand orbiting that basketball. Trying to find that grain of sand without leaving the Earth is analogous to trying to find an Earth-size exoplanet!

So how do scientists do it? The short answer is that they use telescopes. Both Earth-based telescopes and Space-based telescopes. Of the Space-based telescopes, Kepler is the most notable because it is the only telescope so far that was dedicated solely to finding exoplanets. Unfortunately, Kepler malfunctioned in 2013 and is no longer actively collecting data.

How do telescopes find exoplanets? There are several methods, including radial velocity, transit, microlensing, imaging, and pulsar timing. Very few exoplanets have been discovered by imaging, which is directly taking a picture of a planet. This is because most exoplanets are too small and dim to image. Thus, the other methods focus on watching a star and inferring that a planet is there by looking for certain changes in the light that the star is emitting. Most exoplanets have been discovered using two methods: radial velocity and transit. We will discuss these methods in detail.

To understand the radial velocity method, we need to understand the Doppler Effect. The Doppler Effect is the shift in wavelength observed when an object that is giving off light is moving towards you or away from you. First, imagine a star that is not moving. In this scenario, the light that is emitted by the star is exactly what you see. Second, imagine that a star is moving away from you; we say it has a positive radial velocity. In this scenario, the light that you see is longer in wavelength than the light that the star is emitting because it gets stretched out. We call this a redshift, because red light has longer wavelength than other visible light. Please note that this does NOT mean that the star looks red; just that the observed light from the star is at a longer wavelength than what the star is actually emitting. The faster the star is moving away from you, the bigger the redshift. Third, imagine that a star is moving towards you; we say it has a negative radial velocity. In this scenario, the light that you see is shorter in wavelength than the light that the star is emitting because it gets squeezed together. We call this a blueshift, because blue light has shorter wavelength than other visible light. The faster the star is moving towards you, the bigger the blueshift.

Note that the Doppler Effect only happens if the object that is emitting light is moving towards you or away from you. An object that is moving side to side, or perpendicular to your line of sight, will not show any shift.

An object's motion along your line of sight is known as its radial velocity (Figure 19.1). By convention, when an object is moving away from you, we say that it has a positive radial velocity. When an object is moving towards you, we say that it has a negative radial velocity. When an object is moving perpendicular to you, we that is has zero radial velocity. Since the amount of red or blueshift depends on an object's speed, looking at the Doppler Shift of a star gives you its radial velocity.

away from line of sight = positive radial velocity
(REDSHIFT)

towards line of sight = negative radial velocity
(BLUESHIFT)

perpendicular to line of sight = zero radial velocity
(NO DOPPLER SHIFT)

Figure 19.2: Doppler Effect

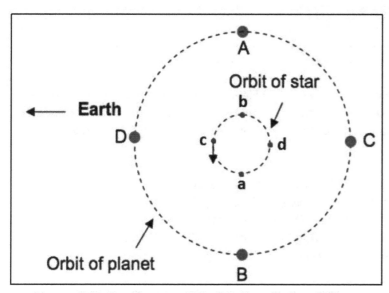

Figure 19.2: Exoplanet and Star Orbiting Center of Mass

How does this apply to exoplanets? We know that planets orbit around stars; but this statement is slightly inaccurate. In reality, what is actually happening is that both the planet and the star are orbiting around the common center of mass (Figure 19.2). Though the planet's orbit is larger than the star's orbit, both the star and the planet move around the center of mass in the same time. So for example, when the planet is at location "A" in Figure 19.2, the star is at location "a". This means that the star and the planet are always at opposite positions in their orbits. Now imagine you are on Earth (which is to

213

the left in Figure 19.2) looking at an edge-on view of this solar system. You can't see the planet; it's too dim. But you can see the star. Note that sometimes the star is going towards you (at "b"), sometimes it is going away from you (at "a"), and sometimes its motion is perpendicular to your line of sight (at "c" and "d"). Thus as you watch the star, you will see its light shift from blueshifted to no shifted to redshifted to no shifted to blueshifted and so forth. Because the star would not do this if it didn't have a planet around it, you can infer that the planet is there. Using the amount of shift, you can calculate the star's exact radial velocity over time. From this information, you can infer the mass of the planet and the planet's distance from the star.

The star's radial velocity curve will look something like shown in Figure 19.e. The peaks correspond to the points when the star is moving at its maximum away from you. The dips corresponds to the points when the star is moving at its maximum towards you. The zero points correspond to when the star is moving neither towards nor away from you; it is moving perpendicular to your line of sight.

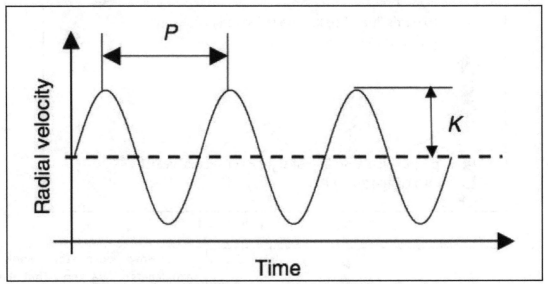

Figure 19.3: Radial Velocity Curve for A Star With an Exoplanet

The period of the radial velocity curve (labeled "P" in Figure 19.3) is the time from peak to peak. It represents how long it takes the star and the planet to complete one orbit. Remember from Kepler's 3rd law that a planet's period depends on its distance. Thus from the period, you can calculate how far the planet is from its star.

The amplitude (labeled "K" in Figure 19.3) is the height of the curve. It depends on the planet's mass, the star's mass, and the planet's distance. The bigger the planet, the bigger the amplitude. This is because the planet will have a greater pull on its star. The smaller the star, the bigger the amplitude. This is because big stars will have more resistance to motion. The closer the planet, the bigger the amplitude. This is because if the planet is closer it will have a greater pull. Thus bigger amplitudes correspond to large planets that are close to small stars.

Besides the radial velocity method, the other common method of exoplanet detection is the transit method. If you are viewing a solar system from an edge-on view, then a planet will occasionally move in front of its star...this is known as a transit. When it does so it will block a little bit of the light coming from the star, and the star's light will become slightly dimmer. This drop in light is typically 0.01%-1%. By detecting and tracking these dips we can infer the presence of a planet and calculate its orbital distance (planets that are further will show more time between dips and wider dips) and its radius (planets that are bigger will cause deeper dips because they block more light).

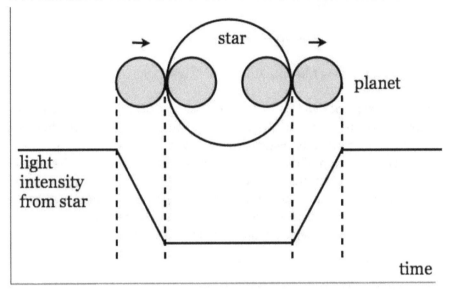

Figure 19.4: Exoplanet Transiting a Star (CAE Astronomy Workshop Materials)

This is the method of detection used by the Kepler space telescope. The Kepler space telescope searched for exoplanets within a cone of 3,000 light years away from the Earth. This is just a very small portion of galaxy, which is 100,000 light years wide. Note that all of the exoplanets that have been discovered are within our galaxy; other galaxies are much too far away for us to detect planets. If you are curious where in the sky this is, look outside at the night sky in the summer. There are three bright stars that form a triangle; this constellation is known as the summer triangle. Kepler's field of view is right at the base of the triangle.

The image shown in Figure 19.4 describes the transit method in more detail. Initially the light coming from the star shows a constant intensity. As the planet begins to pass in front of the star, the intensity dips. It reaches a minimum when the planet is completely in front of the star. When the planet begins to move beyond the star, the intensity will gradually increase back to its maximum.

The transit dip has several features, each which represent different aspects of the planet. The dip depth is determined by how much light is blocked. This is determined by the planet's radius; larger planets will block more light and cause a deeper dip. The width of the dip is determined by how long the transit takes. This is determined by the planet's orbital period; longer orbital periods will lead to a longer transit and cause a wider dip (because the planet is moving slower). The sides of the dip are sloped because it takes some time for the planet to move in front of and out from in front of the star. The bottom of the dip is flat because when the planet is completely in front of the star, it blocks a constant amount of light.

The time from the beginning of one dip to the beginning of the next dip is the time it takes the planet to complete one orbit - the orbital period (Figure 19.5). Remember from Kepler's 3rd Law that the orbital period is determined by the planet's distance from the Sun. Thus planets that are further will have a greater time between dips. Note that the time between dips is always longer than the duration of the dips themselves.

Figure 19.5: Light Curve Showing Multiple Transits of Single Exoplanet

When a star has more than one exoplanet, there will be more than one series of dips that add up. By looking at the plot of star brightness versus time, you can determine how many exoplanets there are and the relative sizes and orbital periods of the planets. Figure 19.7 shows an example of how this works. There are two exoplanets. One causes the pattern of dips that is shallower, the other causes the pattern of dips that is deeper. The deeper dips represent a planet that is bigger and has a shorter orbital period than the other planet. The pattern of dips will add up to produce the brightness curve shown at the bottom. Note that there are times when both planets are in front of the star at the same time; in this case, the dip produced is bigger than the dip the individual planets could have made.

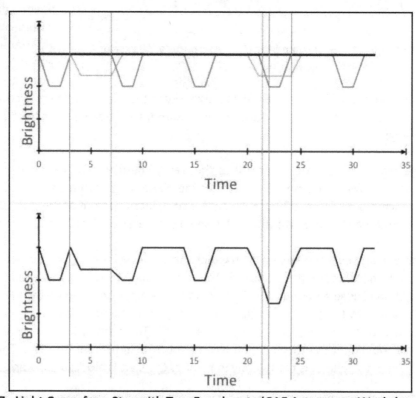

Figure 19.7: Light Curve for a Star with Two Exoplanets (CAE Astronomy Workshop Materials)

216

Questions You Should Be Able to Answer
1. What is the Doppler Effect? When is light from a star redshifted, and when is it blueshifted?
2. How is the radial velocity method used to detect extrasolar planets? What planetary properties can this method determine?
3. How is the transit method used to detect extrasolar planets? What planetary properties can this method determine?

Suggestions for Further Reading
1. http://astro.unl.edu/naap/esp/detection.html (summary of exoplanet detection methods)
2. http://astro.unl.edu/classaction/animations/extrasolarplanets/ca_extrasolarplanets_graph.html (radial velocity animation)
3. http://astro.unl.edu/classaction/animations/extrasolarplanets/transitsimulator.html (transit simulator)

Suggestions for Practice
4. http://astro.unl.edu/interactives/stellarvelocity/stellarVelocity1.html (radial velocity questions)
5. http://astro.unl.edu/interactives/doppler/DopplerShift2.html (doppler shift questions)
6. http://astro.unl.edu/classaction/questions/extrasolarplanets/ca_extrasolarplanets_radialvelocitycurve.html (radial velocity method questions)
7. http://astro.unl.edu/classaction/questions/extrasolarplanets/ca_extrasolarplanets_espdopplershift.html (more radial velocity method questions)
8. http://astro.unl.edu/classaction/questions/extrasolarplanets/ca_extrasolarplanets_ampperiod.html (more radial velocity method questions)

Chapter 19 Activity: Radial Velocity Method

The diagram below shows the orbit of a star with an exoplanet. Questions 1-8 refer to this diagram.

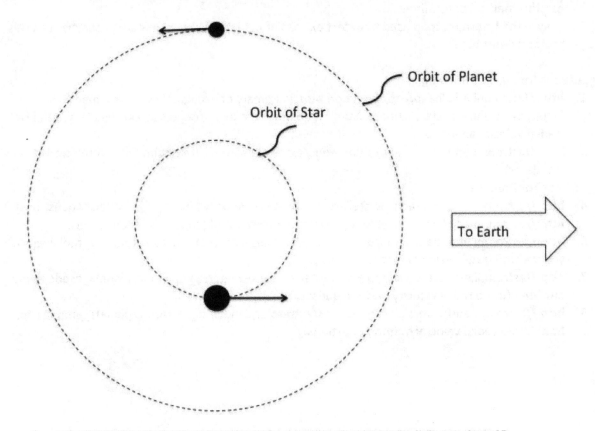

1. What direction is the star moving at the position shown (right, left, up, down)?

2. What direction is the planet moving at the position shown (right, left, up, down)?

3. Circle the correct answer from the italicized choices: the star will always be moving in *the same direction / the opposite direction* as the planet.

4. If an observer on Earth looks at this star, will she see the star's light being redshifted, blueshifted, or not shifted?

5. Two students are discussing their answers to the previous question:
   Student A says, "The planet is moving to the left, away from the star. This means the light will be redshifted."
   Student B says, "But it is the star you see, not the planet. And when the planet is moving to the left, the star is moving in the opposite direction (to the right). This is towards the Earth, so I think the light will be blueshifted."

   Which student(s) do you agree with and why?

6. Draw where the planet will be once it has moved a quarter of the way around on its orbit. Then draw an arrow (either up, down, left, or right) showing which way the planet is moving at that point.

7. Draw where the star will be when the planet is at the position you drew in question 6. Then draw an arrow showing which way the star is moving at that point.

8. When the star is at the location you drew in question 7, will its light be blueshifted, redshifted, or not shifted?

9. Using an " X " mark ALL of the portions of the star's orbit where the light would be redshifted as observed from the Earth.

10. Using an " * " mark ALL of the portions of the star's orbit where the light would be blueshifted as observed from the Earth.

11. Label the location where the star's light would show its maximum redshift with " MR ".

12. Label the location where the star's light would show its maximum blueshift with "MB ".

The diagram below shows the orbit of a star with an exoplanet and the corresponding radial velocity curve for the star. Four locations in the planet's orbit are shown. Questions 9-12 refer to this diagram

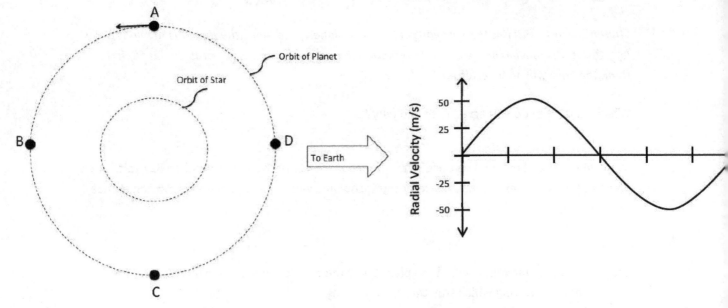

13. For each of the four locations of the planet, mark and label on the star's orbit where the star would be at that time.

14. For each of the four positions of the star, draw arrow to indicate which way the star is moving at that time.

15. For each of the four positions of the star, indicate whether the star's light is redshifted, blueshifted, or not shifted.

16. Mark and label the positions on the radial velocity curve that correspond to the four letters. Remember that positive radial velocities correspond to the star moving away from the Earth!!

The amount of Doppler shift in the star's light is proportion to $\frac{m}{\sqrt{M}d}$, where m is the mass of the planet, M is the mass of the star, and d is the distance between the star and the planet. It will be easier to detect the expolanet the bigger the Doppler shift is.

17. For *each* row below (e.g. A or B, then C or D, then E or F), circle the planet that will be easier to detect, and then fill in your reasoning. m is given in terms of Jupiter's mass, and M is given in terms of the Sun's mass.

		Reasoning
Planet A m = 2.5 M = 1 d = 0.3 AU	**Planet B** m = 2.5 M = 2 d = 0.3 AU	
Planet C m = 0.5 M = 2 d = 1 AU	**Planet D** m = 0.5 M = 2 d = 3 AU	
Planet E m = 3 M = 1 d = 0.8 AU	**Planet F** m = 2 M = 1 d = 0.8 AU	

18. On the plot below, sketch what the radial velocity curves for planets C and D would look like. Be sure to get the relative period and amplitude correct!

radial velocity

time

221

19. Ranks the exoplanets below in terms of easiest to hardest to detect.

Planet	m	M	d
A	2.5	1	0.2
B	2	1	0.6
C	2.5	0.5	0.2
D	1	2	0.7

Chapter 19 Activity: Transit Method

The diagram below shows an exoplanet orbiting a star. Questions 1-5 refer to this diagram.

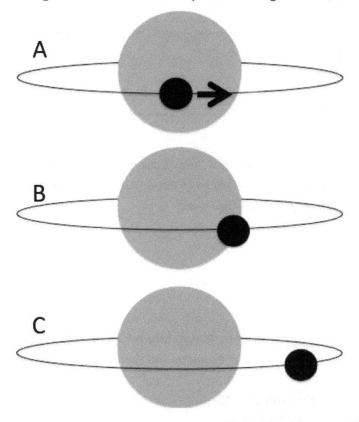

A

B

C

1. Label the diagrams with the appropriate labels from the following options: exoplanet in front of the star, exoplanet partially in front of the star, and exoplanet not in front of the star.

2. In which diagram would you measure the greatest amount of light coming from the star? Label this diagram with the words "greatest amount of light."

3. In which diagram would you measure the least amount of light coming from the star? Label this diagram with the words "least amount of light."

4. In the diagram where the exoplanet is partially in front of the star, describe what the light coming from the star would look like (e.g. would it be getting brighter, getting dimmer, staying constant)?

5. On the transit curve below, mark the positions corresponding to diagrams A, B, and C.

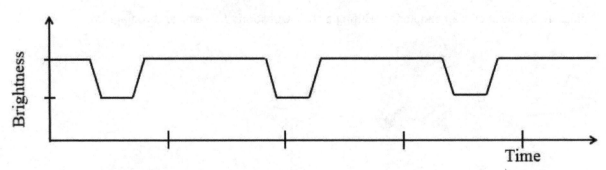

6. If the exoplanet from the previous question were bigger, how would this effect the transit curve? Circle the correct choices from the italicized options and then explain your reasoning.
   a. the period between dips would be *longer / shorter / the same*
   b. the width of the dip would *longer / shorter / the same*
   c. the depth of the dip would be *deeper / shallower / the same*

7. If the exoplanet from the previous question were closer to its star, how would this effect the transit curve? Circle the correct choices from the italicized options and then explain your reasoning.
   a. the period between dips would be *longer / shorter / the same*
   b. the width of the dip would *longer / shorter / the same*
   c. the depth of the dip would be *deeper / shallower / the same*

8. On the diagram below, draw what the transit curve from question 5 would look like if the planet were bigger AND closer to its star.

9. Would it be easier to detect a bigger exoplanet or a smaller exoplanet using the transit method? Explain your reasoning.

10. Would it be easier to detect an exoplanet that is close to its star or one that is further from its star using the transit method? Explain your reasoning. (Hint: think about how the distance effects how often you would see transits.

The diagram below shows a light curve for a star with <u>two</u> transiting planets, one bigger and one smaller.

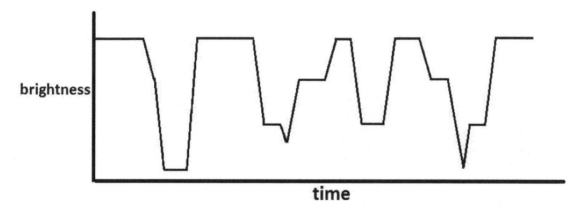

11. Use the letter "A" to label a location where just the bigger planet is in front of the star.

12. Use the letter "B" to label a location where just the smaller planet is in front of the star.

13. Use the letter "C" to label a location where both planets are in front of the star.

14. Which planet is closer to the star – the bigger one or the smaller one?

15. Is there ever a scenario where a star would have an exoplanet but it could not detected? In the diagram below, draw where the observer would be looking from for this to be the case.

Chapter 20: Exoplanet Characteristics

In this chapter, you will learn about the characteristics of known exoplanets.

Let's look first at the sizes of exoplanets. Figure 20.1 shows that there are about 175 Earth-sized planets (less than 1.25 times the Earth's radius), about 300 Super Earth-sized planets (1.25 - 2 times the Earth's radius), about 600 Neptune-sized planets (2 - 6 times the Earth's radius), and about 700 Jupiter-sized planets (greater than 6 times the Earth's radius). This data makes it seem like there are more bigger exoplanets than smaller exoplanets. However, this is probably an observational bias...remember that bigger exoplanets are easier to find because they cause bigger transit dips and larger stellar radial velocities.

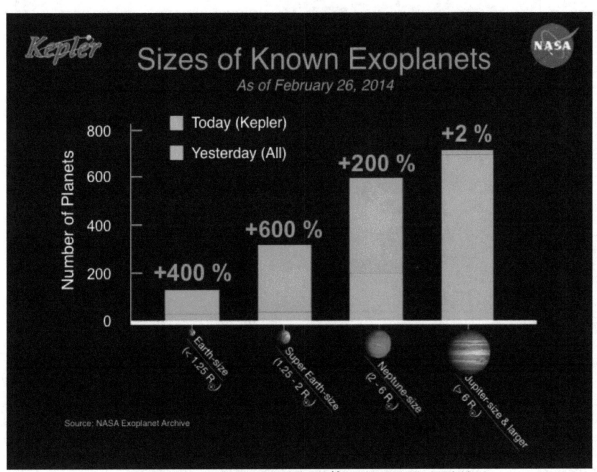

Figure 20.1: Exoplanet Sizes (http://www.nasa.gov, Kepler)

We would also like to look at how far these planets are from their stars. Figure 20.2 plots masses versus distances for all known exoplanets (as of 2014). Different colors represent different detection methods; for example, the planets in light gray were detected by Kepler. On the y-axis are the planets' masses in terms of Jupiter's mass. On the x-axis is the planets' distances from their stars in AU. Jupiter is 1 Jupiter mass and 5 AU, and so plots at the top star in the diagram. Thus planets similar to Jupiter in terms of mass and distance have been found. Earth is 0.003 Jupiter masses and 1 AU, and so plots at the bottom star in the diagram. You can see that though planets similar in size to the Earth have been found, we have not found planets that are similar in both size AND distance to the Earth. Again, this is probably an observational bias. Remember that planets that are close to their stars are easier to identify because they will transit their stars' more often. To find planets that are further away, a longer time period of data is needed, and we don't have enough data yet!

Figure 20.2: Mass Versus Distance of Exoplanets (http://www.exoplanets.org)

We would like to know if any of these planets have the possibility of harboring life. Life as we know it on the Earth appears to need three essential ingredients: an energy source, organic molecules, and liquid water. Any planet orbiting a star automatically has an energy source (the star's energy). Likewise, organic molecules seem to be found pretty much everywhere. Therefore, the limiting factor is liquid water. Thus one way to start to answer the question of life on exoplanets is to look at whether liquid water could exist on these planets' surfaces. To this end, scientists define what is known as the habitable zone. The habitable zone around a star is the zone in which a planet could potentially have liquid water on its surface, provided that the atmosphere pressure is not too high or too low. The diagram in Figure 20.3 shows one estimates for the habitable zone around our Sun. Earth is at the inner edge of the habitable zone; depending on how optimistic you are, Mars may be at the outer edge (as it is in this diagram). The planets interior to the habitable zone are too hot for liquid water and the planets exterior to the habitable zone are too cold for liquid water.

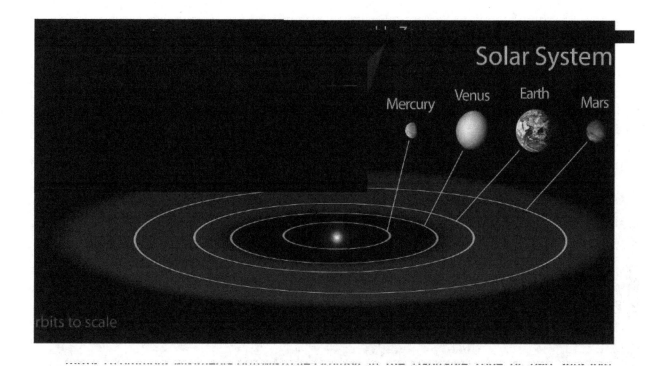

Solar System

Mercury Venus Earth Mars

rbits to scale

The distance of the habitable zone from its star depends on the size of the star (Figure 20.4). If a star is larger than our Sun, it will be hotter, moving the habitable zone further away. If a star is smaller than our Sun, it will be colder, moving the habitable zone closer.

Note that just because a planet is in the habitable zone does not mean it has to have liquid water; it just means that it could. In order to have liquid water, the size of the planet also needs to be within a certain range as well. If a planet is too small, then its interior will cool, its magnetic field will die, and its atmosphere will erode. This is what happened to Mars. If a planet is too large, then there will be too much H and He (it will be a Jovian planet), and the atmosphere will be too hot and the pressure will be too high for liquid water. It's a bit like Goldilocks and the Three Bears; the planet can't be too big, it can't be too small, it can't be too close to its star, and it can't be too far away from its star. It must be just right.

As of June 6, 2018, about thirty potentially habitable Earth-sized planets have been found. A milestone occurred in April of 2014, when the first Earth-sized planet in its star's habitable zone was found. This planet is named Kepler-186f.

Hotter Stars

Sunlike Stars

Cooler Stars

Kepler-186f is about the same size as the Earth, as you can see in the to-scale comparison in Figure 20.5. Note that we do not actually have a picture of Kepler-186f – it is much too small to photograph. The image here (and virtually all images of exoplanets you will see in the news) is an artist's conception. The diagram in Figure 20.5 also compares the Earth's solar system with Kepler-186f's solar system. The star in Kepler-186f's solar system is smaller and colder than our star, and so Kepler-186f is located closer to its star than we are to the Earth. Kepler-186f is 0.36 AU from its star, orbits its star once every 130 Earth days, and is located about 500 light years away from the Earth. There are 4 other planets in Kepler-186f's solar system.

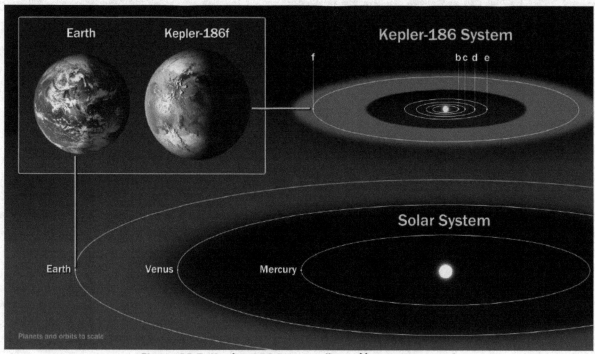

Figure 20.5: Kepler-186 System (http://www.nasa.gov)

We can use the statistics of known exoplanets to estimate the number of habitable planets. Statistics suggest that 1 in 6 stars have an Earth-sized planet, and that 5% of these are in the habitable zone. There are somewhere between 100 and 400 billion stars in our galaxy. This means that there should be somewhere between 17 billion and 67 billion Earth-sized planets in our galaxy and that there should be between 833 million to 3 billion habitable planets...just in our galaxy alone!!

Questions You Should Be Able to Answer
1. Are most exoplanets that have been discovered bigger or smaller than the Earth?
2. What is a habitable zone?
3. How does the size and distance of a habitable zone around a star depend on the temperature of the star?
4. Are habitable planets common in our galaxy?

Suggestions for Further Reading
29. http://planetquest.jpl.nasa.gov (NASA-JPL exoplanet website)

Common Pitfalls
-Just because a planet is in the habitable zone does not mean it definitely has life, or even liquid water on the surface. It just means there *could* be liquid water if other conditions (like the size of the planet) are just right as well.

Chapter 20 Activity: Habitable Zone

Part 1: Our Sun's Habitable Zone

Earth is the only planet known to harbor life of any kind, past or present. As part of the search for evidence of life on other planets, both in our Solar System and in other planetary systems, we are looking not just for evidence of living organisms themselves, but for evidence of the conditions that might even be hospitable to life as we know it. One feature that astronomers consider to determine whether a planet MIGHT have the conditions necessary for life as we know it is whether the planet falls within the 'habitable zone' of its host star. The habitable zone is defined as the region around a star where temperatures could allow for liquid water to exist on the surface of a planet if the planet's atmospheric pressure is large enough.

Because stars change (they grow brighter slowly over time, expand suddenly, and then die), the position of the habitable zone changes with time. The diagrams at the end of this tutorial show how the Sun's habitable zone will change over time (these are from http://astro.unl.edu/naap/habitablezones/animations/stellarHabitableZone.html). Times listed are in billion of years after Sun formation. For example, 5 Byr means 5 billion years after the Sun forms. The Sun will die somewhere between 10 and 12 Byr.

1. We are currently at about 4.5 Byr. Which planet(s) fall within the habitable zone?

2. Planets interior to the habitable zone are too hot for liquid water. Which planet(s) currently fall within this area?

3. Planets exterior to the habitable zone are too cold for liquid water. Which planet(s) currently fall within this area?

4. Will the Earth always be in the habitable zone? If not, at what age will Earth no longer be in this zone, and how long will that be *from now*?

5. Are there any planets that are not currently in the habitable zone but will be in the future? If so, which planet(s) and when will they be in this zone?

6. If a planet or moon is in the habitable zone, does that automatically mean it has life? Why or why not? (Hint: The Earth's moon is in the habitable zone).

7. If a planet or moon is not in the habitable zone, does that automatically mean it doesn't have life? Why or why not?

8. Two students are discussing their answers to the previous two questions. With which student(s) do you agree and why?

   Student A says, *"Just because something is in the habitable zone doesn't mean it has life. The size of the planet or moon matters as well - the Earth's moon is in the habitable zone, but it's not big enough to have an atmosphere, so it doesn't have life. But you do need water to have life. So if something is not in the habitable zone, there is no way it can have life."*

   Student B says, *"But what about Europa? That's definitely not in the habitable zone, and there's no water on the surface, but there might be water deep down kept warm by tidal heating. I don't think the habitable zone means definitively that a planet has or doesn't have life. I think it is just a guideline scientists use as a starting point to figure out whether a planet is likely to have life or not.*

Part 2: History of Life on Earth

The timeline below shows how life developed on Earth.

Billions of Years Ago	Event
4.5	Earth Forms
3.8	First Life (single-celled bacteria)
1.5	Multi-Celled Organisms
0.45	Land Animals
0.065	Dinosaurs Go Extinct
0.0005	Human Life

9. For each event in the timeline above, determine how long after the formation of the Earth this event occurred. Then calculate what fraction of its current age (4.5 Byr) the Earth was at that time. Fill in your answers in the table below. As an example, the Earth formed 4.5 billion years ago and multi-celled organisms formed 1.5 billion years ago, so this is when the Earth was 3 billion years old (4.5-1.5), and is 66.7% of the Earth's current age (3/4.5 x 100).

Age of Earth	% of Earth's Current Age	Event
		Earth Forms
		First Life (single-celled bacteria)
3	66.7%	Multi-Celled Organisms
		Land Animals
		Dinosaurs Go Extinct
		Human Life

10. We often think about dinosaurs as being really old and ancient forms of life. Is that an accurate way to think?

Part 3: Other Solar Systems

Stars are classified by mass, and the size of a star will affect the habitable zone. Bigger stars are typically hotter; this means that the habitable zone will be located further away from the star. Additionally, bigger stars have shorter lifetimes than smaller stars, and this will affect the length of time that planets can remain habitable. The table below shows an estimate of the orbit size of the longest habitable planet and the habitable lifetime of that planet for different types of stars.

Star Type	Star Mass (in terms of Sun's mass)	Orbit Size of Longest Habitable Planet (AU)	Habitable Lifetime (in billions of years)	Most Advanced Life that Could Develop
O	16	190	0.012	
B	5	20	0.19	
A	2	5	1.2	
F	1.3	1.7	5.0	
G	1	1.1	7.0	
K	0.7	0.5	27	
M	0.4	0.2	165	

11. Fill in the last column in the above table to indicate the most advanced form of life that could develop around each star based on the habitable lifetime estimate.

12. What type of star is our Sun (hint: the star mass in the table is in terms of the Sun's mass)?

13. Compare to our Sun's type, what do you think the development of life would be like on planets orbiting stars that are bigger than our Sun?

14. Compare to our Sun's type, what do you think the development of life would be like on planets orbiting stars that are smaller than our Sun?

15. Bigger stars are easier to detect and monitor because they are brighter. Which type of star is the brightest, and which is the dimmest?

16. Given your answers to the above questions, which type of stars do you think NASA should direct its attention to when search for life beyond Earth?